REDRESSING THE BALANCE:
A Commonsense Approach to Causation

REDRESSING THE BALANCE:

A Commonsense Approach to Causation

PAUL DIFFORD

Institute of Industrial Accident Investigators
Research & Development Centre, England

ACCIDENTAL BOOKS
www.accidentalbooks.co.uk

Published by
Accidental Books Ltd
29 Meadow park
Wembdon
Bridgwater
Somerset
TA6 7QE

www.accidentalbooks.co.uk

Ordering Information
Available from book shops and on-line at www.accidentalbooks.co.uk

Printed in Great Britain.

British Library Cataloguing in Publication Data. A catalogue record for this book is available from the British Library.

ISBN: 978-0-9570411-0-3

To commonsense....*since those who deny it deny not only logic and science, but the very notion of the reasonable man himself.*

FOREWORD

by
Trevor Williams,
Executive Committee Chairman,
Institute of Industrial Accident Investigators

In 1998, under contract with Neucom, the Institute (IIAI) initiated its first Ten Year Study. Aside a goal of identifying and harmonising the key subjects that an international community of investigators might utilise and draw from, a range of critical questions were posed. In particular, one such question was *"what, exactly, should certain grades of IIAI member know about current models of causation?"*

Following Difford's (1998; 2004) reports, my committee agreed that reference to Heinrich (1941) and Bird (1974) would suffice since those effectively present contrary views on cause. The Chief Examiner felt that an understanding of them, transferred by suitable instructors, would highlight the matter of bias and promote objectivity in both evidence gathering and analysis. Difford (1998) also analysed Petersen's (1971) multiple causation theory and Reason's (1997) Swiss cheese model (SCM) but rejected those as ill-founded. As a result, a decision not to reference the SCM in IIAI courses has never changed. However, reference to it was made in the 2010 IIAI Diploma sessions in order, simply, to ensure awareness of its existence and general philosophy. As regards that reference, the following is a summary as it relates to certain elements of the subject herein.

The philosophy of the organisational accident or management failure school is grounded in Petersen (1971) and the SCM is the result of a desperate attempt to combine the models of Heinrich and Bird; generally, the following is typical of the school's beliefs and practices:-

- They are convinced, illogically and quite absurdly, that the multiple factors invariably involved in all accidents are always transitively causative;

- They are unable to distinguish between causes and conditions;

- Ridiculously, they see management as being the sole cause of a man's behaviour, errors and violations (at least in work);

- They believe that accidents cannot happen but for multiple failures of barriers and defences;

- They suffer heavily from an illogical and irrational overdose of hindsight bias and confirmation bias;

- They unwittingly compel organisations to reactive fire-fighting;

- They employ academically invented terms unaware that they conceal a counter-productive and reprehensibly blame-laden philosophy;

- They strip all accidents of context and relentlessly attribute causes to situations (blaming upstream individuals in the process) rather than address the essence of the parts played by those directly involved;

- They stifle the developments that have been made in the behavioural sciences in the belief that they alone understand the causes of, and remedies for, all forms of human behaviour;

- Aligned, certainly in the UK, to a flawed regulatory perspective on cause, they persistently focus on the organisation or management.

Following an academic response, I requested Paul (Difford) to re-submit his 1998 and 2004 rejections of Petersen, Bird and Reason as a more detailed (albeit as concise as possible in this edition) case for their on-going refutation (this book being the result). Whilst relevant IIAI materials will still reference Heinrich and Bird (despite Bird's model being rejected for similar reasons to its modern day equivalent...the SCM), those will be tempered by Difford's New Millennium Theory. In that respect, this book provides the substance and justification for future IIAI references to Difford's Theory. Furthermore, it lays the ground for his model which is the only systems and error analysis tool ever approved by us. Inter alia, it highlights the means by which the numerous problems reported to the TYS as being created by 'most' of the Root Cause Analysis models (hard form and software) circulating the market place are either disposed of or, ideally, avoided altogether.

In arriving at where certain practitioners and academics are today (i.e. in a state of confusion regarding cause and remedy), it was clear that the numerous models etc found by Difford could have occupied all of his book. Therefore, none but those that are necessary for his purposes here are identified. His purpose is not to judge or compare except where such will inform the risk management and investigative communities. Such judgement, massively overdue, is essential given that the safety and security of man, his environment and the quality of an organisation's outputs are currently compromised by myth.

As regards a balanced discussion, that was impossible and Difford has made no attempt in that respect. The bias (for want of a better word) that prevents the occupation by all parties of the objective middle ground is truly enormous. To say that the bias is wholly one-sided and illogically out of balance would be an understatement. Therefore, as an attempt to redress the balance, do not consider what unfolds below as a 'cherry picking' exercise. All other arguments (and I use the word argument incredibly loosely) are essentially to the contrary in that they reside, juxtaposed to the arguments herein, on the other side of the fence. Within the following text, therefore, lies the argument that you have not heard before and I am certain that it will generate the debate that is so desperately needed if we are ever to see a logical and commonsense approach to the causes of industrial accidents.

Before leaving you to consider the many issues that Difford raises and deals with, he is but the messenger. Much of what follows has been written on the walls for decades; indeed, bleeding through the occasional whitewash, some of it has been there for centuries.

Trevor Williams
IIAI Executive Committee Chairman.

PREFACE

A Few Words from the Author to Set the Scene

The secret of science is to ask the right question
(Tizard 1885-1959)

There are many who believe that management or organisational failures are the root causes of all accidents. However, philosophers, experts in agent causation and causation in law disagree; indeed, such experts find those claims ridiculous and absurd. Commonsense, logic, empirical data, International courts, the Council of the EU, UK Parliaments and Law Commission (to name just a few) also disagree.

Fortunately, following objective reconsideration, even the staunchest supporters of the management failure or organisational accident school (the two being synonymous of course) are forced to concede that management cannot possibly cause all accidents. Unfortunately, the original belief is so engrained and overriding that it comes irrepressibly to the fore during their 'investigations'. In consequence, they pursue their central causal enquiries as if the default belief were true even though they have conceded that it is not.

When challenged to logically justify their invariable and unconditional findings, they, like the philosophies, models and theories upon which they rely, cannot. But, when the right questions are posed, as they are throughout this book, the organisational accident school reveals itself to be a fanciful construct devoid of either foundation or substance.

As you read on, take the following with you. If the opening belief is wrong, then any philosophy, model or theory presenting the same must also be wrong. That is undeniable and irrefutable.

Paul Difford

CONTENTS

Chapter Five Part 2: A Notion of Cause that is Absurd in both Practice and Principle

Chapter Six: Reason's (1997) Swiss Cheese Model

INTRODUCTION

Crime and Multiple Causation

According to Italian physician and criminal anthropologist Lombroso (1911:1)...

"every crime has its origin in a multiplicity of causes, often intertwined and confused, each of which we must, in obedience to the necessities of thought and speech, investigate singly. The multiplicity is generally the rule with human phenomena, to which one can almost never assign a single cause unrelated to others".

Lombroso's view, advocating multiple causation (Gottfredson & Hirschi 1990:48), falls within what is known as the *positivist* school of thought. For positivists, criminal behaviour is not determined by free will but, by a multitude of factors and forces that are outside of the individual's control; e.g. indirect heredity (i.e. behaviour acquired elsewhere or by contact or association with others), matters of psychology, social conditions and environments (Hollin 2002:23). Of course, where there is one school of thought, there will always be others. For instance, classical theorists such as eighteenth century economist Cesare Beccaria and British philosopher Jeremy Bentham disagree with the *positivist* assumptions. For them, humans are rational beings who are able to choose and control their behaviour. Classical theorists see decisions to commit criminal acts as stemming from free will assessments of the gains and losses involved; if the payoff is perceived to be greater than the penalty it might bring, the likelihood of committing a criminal act increases (Hollin 2002:8).

Of course, and as correct as it is, the philosopher's view is slightly underspecified here. When a man determines his action according to the penalty that it might bring, he also considers the likelihood of any adverse consequence materialising and/or the likelihood that his act, having assumed that any adverse consequence will not materialise, will go undetected. As Bentham has put it...

*"Nature has placed mankind under the governance of two sovereign masters, **pain** and **pleasure**. It is for them alone to point out what we ought to do, as well as to determine what we shall do. On the one hand the standard of right and wrong, on the other the chain of causes and effects, are fastened to their throne. They govern us in all we do, in all we say, in all we think..."* (Burns & Hart 1996:11)

The law reflects the above statement and most philosophers accept that behaviour is not determined by external forces to the extent that blame could be considered unjustified in the criminal context (Ashworth 1999:27); indeed, knowledge of intrinsic forces does little more than provide explanations or reasons for behaviour to most central causal enquiries. The UK Parliament, for example, is similarly opined where individual criminal responsibility is the subject (see s.7-8, & 36-37 of the Health and Safety at Work Act 1974). Nonetheless, we will see that some such as Petersen (1971), Bird (1974) and Reason (1997), who are neither authorities nor experts in the fields of philosophy or causation, believe that organisation's are the sole determinant, and hence cause, of man's behaviour at work. Despite the fact that only a truthful statement from the person involved could answer a question regarding what caused their behaviour (Hart & Honore 2002), some are intent on answering it for them. However...

"...in things that are within the reach of every man's understanding, and upon which the whole conduct of human life turns, the philosopher must follow the multitude, or make himself perfectly ridiculous"
(Reid 1764)

Epidemiology and Multiple Causation

Regardless of individual views on the debate surrounding the cause of crime or at risk behaviour, few would expect epidemiology to do anything other than exhaust all possible lines of enquiry into the incidence of disease that could wipe out entire populations. Over time, to better express the apparently 'complex reality of multicausality', epidemiologists began thinking in terms of chains of causation (Duncan 1988). Later, these already complex chains would be accused of suffering from the "defect of oversimplification" and a more complex model would emerge entitled the "web of causation" (MacMahon et al 1960). Consequently, multiple causation was now being expressed by way of *metaphor*. However, finding that things had gone too far (i.e. become too multivariate and complex, devoid of scientific basis), some were compelled to enquire into the whereabouts of the 'spider' responsible for the web of causation's vast array of factors. Such enquiry was desperately needed since epidemiology was often appearing to be "more concerned with intricately modelling complex relationships among risk factors than with understanding their origins and implications" (Krieger 1994:887).

In a similar vein, to assist the industrial accident prevention community into this new millennium, critical questions will be raised and answered below in relation to the confused and complex 'webs' that result from many academics and safety practitioner's reliance on notions of 'multiple causation theory' in the general industrial setting. In particular, we will consider Petersen's (1971) theory on multiple causation, Heinrich's accident causation theory, Bird's (1974) updated sequence and Reason's (1997: 2004) so-called Swiss cheese model (SCM). Supporters of the *metaphor* that is the SCM (e.g. Reason, Hollnagel and Paries 2006: referred to from here on in as Reason et al 2006) for instance consider the highly logical and simplistic cause-effect relationship shown by 'proper theory' to be in error and inadequate. For them, a "more powerful representation" is required that is *at least* as complex as a "causal network" (Hollnagel 2004:58); which, as we shall see, is the cause of industry's problem in a nutshell. Driven by academic invention in the face of irrefutable evidence to the contrary, industry has become unwittingly and obsessively pre-occupied with contrived and spurious relationships, coincidences and mere conditions. Consequently, the real causes of industrial accidents are going unaddressed.

Chapter One

Chapter One commences to look at what was, for purposes here, the effective starting point of the problem; that is, Petersen's (1971; 1978) multiple causation theory and his ill-founded assumption that management or organisational failures cause *all* accidents. Gordon (1949) had earlier laid certain ground to assist the confusion by way of his belief that epidemiology's triad (i.e. host, agent, environment) could shed light on the causes of accidents; however, that will be dealt with and disposed of separately in Chapter Four.

In addition to Petersen, Chapter One also takes an introductory look at Heinrich's (1931) accident causation theory, his common cause hypothesis and his finding that unsafe acts caused 88% of the accidents in his study. Pausing to consider the common cause hypothesis by way of a number of worked examples, we find that it makes clear and logical sense and is in keeping with the reasonable man's view of things in the real world; despite which, Petersen rejects it and the essence of Heinrich's findings. However, having also turned to consider empirical evidence regarding the causes of accidents in a number of major jurisdictions, we find that Petersen's rejection of the common cause hypothesis was erroneous and that all empirical data was, and remains to be, contrary to his notion of multiple causation.

Chapter Two

Nonetheless, many today still genuinely believe that there will always be numerous causes (both root and immediate) of any accident. Consequently, Chapter Two looks at the first of the reasons for this mistaken belief insofar as it relates to an absence of logic and the inability to draw the most basic of the critical distinctions that exist between causes and conditions.

Whilst here, this book makes reference to root cause, underlying cause and proximate cause. For purposes within this text, and only within this text, those terms mean the same thing; i.e. they mean *the cause*.

Chapter Three

Chapter Three takes a closer at Heinrich's accident causation theory. Whilst he makes the only supportable statement of cause ever to have been made prior to Difford' (1998) modification of it (TYS), he opted to depict the accident sequence as a row of dominoes (see fig.I1).

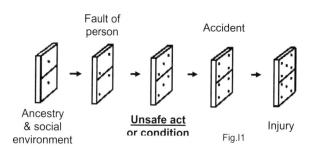

Fig.I1

Unfortunately, the additional factors that he incorporated by way of at least one of the dominoes allude to a finding of cause that he cannot possibly have made. In fact, he proposes an invariable and unconditional causal sequence that detracts from the proximate causes that he factually identified; which was, that 88% of accidents are caused solely by unsafe acts. Consequently, and whilst fully supportive of the essence of Heinrich's theory, we will see (amongst other things) why his five domino sequence reduces logically to just three...if not just two.

Unaware of the 'causal' over specification created by Heinrich's five domino sequence, many later writers (e.g. Bird 1974 and Reason 1997) followed suit and installed five or more dominoes or slices of Swiss cheese into their models. Of course, they were then compelled to label them. Consequently, as members of the management failure or organisational accident school, the labels became system or safety indicators (i.e. workplace inspection or audit headings). For purposes here, we can also say that each of those indicators fall neatly under a heading of either Man, Machine, Management or Environment; or, in the original epidemiological parlance, host, agent and environment.

Chapter Four

Unaware that their view of cause was largely due to the inability to differentiate between causes and conditions, many embraced the irresistibly attractive epidemiological 'belief' that numerous factors interacted and combined to cause all accidents. Obviously, such a belief was consistent with the pre-existing (but erroneous) view that accidents had multiple causes; not surprisingly then, many believed that epidemiology had directed them to the identification of those causes. However, Chapter Four takes a relatively close look at the science of epidemiology and finds that the original triad had (a). proved problematic for the epidemiological community, and (b). that leading writers of the day such as Suchman (1961; 1970) had specifically warned against its use in any enquiry seeking to determine the cause of behaviour. Indeed, we find that Suchman had warned that it would only identify things that were associated with accidents, not 'things' that were causative of them; that is, its use would identify conditions, *not causes*.

Chapter Four then moves on to consider the UK Health & Safety Executive's (HSE) offerings on error and behaviour and finds it ill-informed, highly misleading and questionable in a number of respects. Not least, we find that Government funded body to be in full support of not only the knowingly debatable but, the unacceptably vague and unworkable assumptions of Reason (1990; 1997); worse still, relating to *the* critical aspect of Reason's Swiss cheese model, we find it to be Reason himself who considers it unacceptably vague and unworkable.

Chapter Five

In Chapter Five, we consider the effective starting point of the management failure movement which, for purposes here, is Bird's (1974) model. This model, resulting from Bird's relabeling of the dominoes in a Heinrich type sequence, shows a loss of control by management as being the starting point for *all* accidents (see fig.I2).

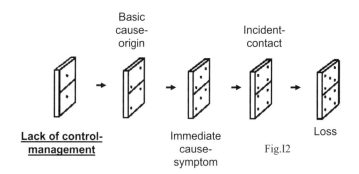

Basic cause-origin

Incident-contact

Lack of control-management

Immediate cause-symptom

Loss

Fig.12

However, Bird provides nothing by way of support for his belief and we find, quite early on, that it is based solely on the epidemiological triad (plus a fourth component in management of course) and multiple causation theory; which, even at this point in time for the astute reader, might be sounding suspiciously like one and the same thing. That is, saying that everything managerial, environmental and mechanical combines to cause accidents is no different to saying that accidents have multiple causes.

Of course, we will see that any model or theory that makes such an invariable and unconditional causative statement is expressing a belief (whether genuinely held or out of necessity) that 'sharp-end' man is never the cause of his own behaviour. Indeed, we find that writers such as Petersen, Bird and Reason are, in fact, compelled into absurdity and the categoric denial that workers have either right, inclination or opportunity to exercise free-will in the workplace. For them, error and violation are always the consequences of managerial or organisational failings. However, and regardless of whether we look to man himself, experts in agent causation or the majority of philosophers, we find nothing but rejection for such notions.

Nonetheless, we find yet again that the UK HSE were quick to adopt, and maintain, a highly questionable philosophy that should have been recognised by them as being contrary to the information on cause that they held (and hold) and upon which they could logically rely.

7

Having already found that the absurdity of the management failure school's exceptionless causal sequence is partly created by denials of free-will and (from Chapter Two) the inability to distinguish between causes and conditions, this Chapter shows that other equally critical rules regarding how we trace causes are also being ignored; indeed, we will see that certain theories *have* to ignore them since to admit them would disprove them.

Chapter Six

Chapter Six deals with a range of issues. Not least, it deals with Reason's (1997; 2004) so-called Swiss cheese model (SCM); what Difford (2004) has referred to as the "theory full of holes" (fig.scm2).

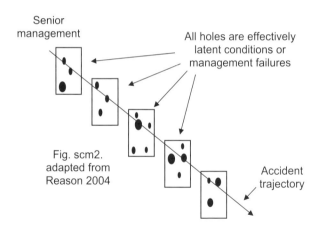

Senior management

All holes are effectively latent conditions or management failures

Fig. scm2. adapted from Reason 2004

Accident trajectory

This is found to be based more or less exclusively (its additional component being the 'resident pathogen') on a desperate attempt to combine Heinrich's theory with the view put forward by Bird (1974); indeed, Bird's updated view was itself effectively attempting to combine Heinrich and Petersen. Not surprisingly therefore, we find that it is heavily reliant on Petersen's (1971) multiple causation theory in addition to the equally unsupportable view that workers are never the cause of their own behaviour.

Whilst a number of the SCM's claims and components are dealt with in general, the primary points upon which the SCM premise rests are disproved by the time we get to Chapter Six. Consequently, an emphasis is placed on Reason's belief that a thing called an *organisational* accident exists that is distinct from an *individual* accident. However, we will find that such a distinction cannot be made and that there is, in fact, no such thing as an organisational accident (it being an academically *miscalculated* invention). In addition, we find that the mechanism via which the SCM convinces itself and users that such a distinction exists results in an exceptionless (i.e. invariable and unconditional or logically invalid) causal statement that experts in jurisprudence had already declared to be absurd. That mechanism, the so-called and epidemiologically flavoured *resident pathogen metaphor*, (AKA the latent failure or latent condition) will render itself ridiculous.

By way of an example to assist here; imagine that I were to say that 17.42 + 33.31 equals 90. Obviously, you would say "no it does not, it equals 50.73". However, I insist that it does equal 90 and give you *my* calculator so that you can retry the calculation. Happy to entertain me, if only to prove me wrong, you enter the sum into *my* calculator (the only one of its kind in existence); but, mysteriously and illogically, the result appears as 90! Despite the fact that you write the sum out on paper and then try 1000 other calculators which all display the answer as 50.73, I say "that is irrelevant, you must use my calculator because my theory is that 17.42 + 33.31 equals 90 and my calculator proves *you* wrong". Clearly, that would be bordering on insanity and you would not entertain me.

In essence, that is the problem that the management failure and organisational accident schools refuse to acknowledge; however, we will find that the SCM calculator is, indeed, absurdly and ridiculously faulty...irreparably so.

Chapter Seven

Finally, some 'concluding comments' are offered that lead naturally to Difford's (2010) New Millennium Theory and a number of supporting principles. By the time the reader arrives there it will be obvious that the new theory *cannot* co-exist with the relevant offerings of Petersen, Bird and Reason. Consequently, the new theory is a formal statement that their models and theories have been rejected and disproved.

In closing here, neither Petersen's multiple causation theory nor Bird's updated sequence made any attempt to validate (not that such can be validated) the exceptionless causal statements that they made; that is, they did not discuss, in the purely causal context, how management could possibly cause all accidents. Their beliefs were founded in their safety backgrounds and were, therefore, perhaps understandable in the interests of prevention.

However, Professor Reason is an academic. Since his SCM was a restatement of Petersen and Bird, he was compelled by academic necessity to attempt, without realising it, to validate the invalid; as it was, he succeeded only in confirming his belief that organisations cause all accidents. Not surprisingly then, he too (by declaring within his book that it was not the place to become embroiled in the philosophy of causation) avoided the critical argument; however, as we now progress on, it will become clear that the SCM was, and always will be, completely out of its depth in any such argument.

Chapter One:
The Causes of Accidents – Singularly Common or Multifactorially Unique?

An Introduction to Heinrich's Accident Causation Theory

In 1931, H.W. Heinrich presented a theory on the causes of industrial accidents. Due to the way in which he portrayed things, it became popularly (albeit, as we shall see, wholly erroneously) referred to as the Domino Theory.

Following an extensive study (touched on immediately below and discussed in more detail later) Heinrich found that 88% of the accidents had been caused by unsafe acts of people, 10% by mechanical or physical hazards (i.e. unsafe conditions) and 2% by acts of God. Of course, as many (Haddon *et al* 1964:252; Difford 1998) have pointed out and the TYS confirms, Heinrich's distinction was somewhat misleading since an unsafe condition can only result from an unsafe act (or omission to act). Nonetheless, and acts of God aside, Heinrich correctly proposed that accidents were caused by unsafe acts and/or conditions ('unsafe acts etc'). However, a common, if not 'convenient', misperception is that this in some way equates to a theory that blames front-line workers; *but, that is not the case* (Difford 1998). Heinrich (1941:16) argued that understanding the reasons why unsafe acts are committed would allow "safety work" to expand into the "underlying field of human behaviour". Properly understood, the theory lays the ground for appropriate remedial intervention strategies to assist all 'levels' of workers, including those whose responsibility might be clouded by, or at the boundaries of, the veil of incorporation (Difford 2004). Whilst some organisations and their employees are already reaping the rewards of this realisation, others have misapplied it and some (predominantly in the so-called 'high risk' sectors) have ignored it to their detriment in favour of the academic notion that organisations, not people, cause all accidents (TYS).

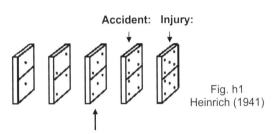

Accident: Injury:

Fig. h1
Heinrich (1941)

Remove domino number **3,** the unsafe act and/or condition, and a preventable accident *cannot* happen.

For Heinrich, accident prevention was a matter of common sense and, for most of us, undeniable logic (TYS). If there is no unsafe act etc then, acts of God aside, there can be no injury or loss (Fig.h1). That said, many (Haddon et al 1964:252) have argued that even the act of God label can conceal a great deal of unwise behaviour as regards precautions that people could have taken (e.g. driving slower when ice on the road could easily have been anticipated; or, sheltering properly from lighting when storms were clearly imminent). In that sense, the more science learns about acts of God, the more they tend to become acts of man; indeed, certain forms of human behaviour are far less predictable and controllable than any act of God (Suchman 1960:243).

Heinrich's Common Cause Hypothesis

Heinrich's study involved 75,000 accidents (Heinrich et al 1980). Amongst other things, having also considered the accidents in groups of the *same kind or type*, Heinrich (1941:31) concluded that the "predominant causes" of near-miss accidents and major-injury accidents were, in the average case, the same. As Suchman (1961:252) for instance notes from Fansler's (1959) study of road traffic accidents, the chain of circumstances are the same regardless of whether the outcome is a collision or a near-miss.

Heinrich's finding has become known as the 'common cause hypothesis' (Wright & van der Schaaf 2004) and it is something that we must have a clear understanding of. For example, imagine that a person trips, for no real reason, whilst walking towards a window in their home that they intend to open. Imagine that they detect the trip in progress and manage to regain their balance...narrowly avoiding (purely by chance or luck) a nasty collision with the corner of the wall or the window reveal.

Dominoes 1-4 (the accident or near-miss accident sequence) have been engaged but, due to the absence of any injury or loss, domino 5 has not come into play.

Now, imagine the same scenario where, for no particular reason on this occasion, the person does not correct themselves in time and a collision with the corner of the wall results along with a major-injury in the form of a huge cut on their forehead and a bloody nose.

On this occasion, dominoes 1-5 have all been engaged and we have a fully completed injury or loss sequence. However, as far as dominoes 1-4 are concerned, the events and circumstances (hence, the cause) are the same as they were in the earlier accident or near-miss; it is only the outcome that has, *by chance*, been different (See Fig. nma1).

Now, consider the same general scenario as in the previous two examples; but, this time, instead of injuring their forehead, imagine that the person has struck their temple on the corner of the wall and, tragically, died.

Whilst the outcomes were markedly different in the fatality, the major-injury and the near-miss, the proximate cause (or root or underlying if you like) was one of human behaviour and was the same (i.e. common) in each. To assist later, note also therefore that Heinrich's 'common cause hypothesis' is neither related to, nor affected by, outcome or severity.

Whilst we will look at two more examples shortly below, it should be obvious that we cannot group say slip, trip and fall accidents with those that involve say building collapses, equipment failure or car crashes. Whilst human behaviour will be the common and proximate cause of each, the physical manifestation of the unsafe act or the circumstances created by an omission to act will vary from accident to accident. Consequently, if we are to properly analyse and learn from accidents, they must be grouped in like-for-like categories of the same kind or type. Once they are, properly trained analysts or investigators can isolate the point in a task or process where a specifiable act or omission would be (or was) injurious or damaging.

As an aside, and whilst general industry data can sometimes inform a number of different organisations, the data being analysed should be unique to the organisation in question.

Accident:

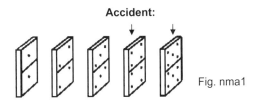

Fig. nma1

The accident or near-miss accident sequence involves only dominoes 1-4. An injury or loss producing accident sequence involves all 5 dominoes. Note here then that the *accident* and the *injury* are two distinct occurrences; one is the result of the other. Often, it is a matter of chance as to whether injury or loss results; indeed, chance often has a large part to play in severity as well.

We will look closer at Heinrich's individual dominoes later below in Chapter Three.

Heinrich's Injury Severity Ratios

Aware that exact figures would never be known, Heinrich concluded that the number of near-miss accidents occurring in an organisation would be consistently higher than the number of injury accidents that occurred. From the data available to him, Heinrich (1941:27:31) therefore *estimated* that in a unit group of 330 "man failure" accidents, one would result in major-injury, 29 in minor-injury and 300 in no injury at all. As with many today (HSE 1997b), he wanted to graphically portray the data and did so via a pyramid or triangle (Fig. ht). However, it should be noted that, here, Heinrich was attempting to focus industry on the need to prevent accidents rather than just injuries since a sole focus on the latter was akin to closing the stable door after the horse had bolted. Consequently, the key message in his triangle (especially in view of the common cause hypothesis) relates to the importance of the near-miss.

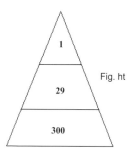

Fig. ht

According to Difford (2004), Heinrich's key message has generally been missed. As it was in Heinrich's time, the level of organisational *and regulatory* response to an accident is largely determined by the severity of its outcome (TYS); indeed, accidents are usually defined in relation to the injury (Roberts et al 1992) or loss (Difford 2004) that results even though neither is necessary to define the accident phenomenon itself (Suchman 1961:243). Such knee-jerk reactions tend to base their remedial intervention strategies on data from *but one* 'injury' accident. However, the sheer number of near-miss accidents affords numerous opportunities for prevention (Bird 1974:18) (a statement, incidentally, that Bird can only make if he accepts the 'common cause hypothesis'). As Suchman (1961:246) puts it...

"It is our contention that any individual is constantly having accidents, and that we can learn a great deal about this phenomenon by studying all accidents rather than only those that result in a reportable injury. This point is especially relevant to accident prevention because we are interested in decreasing the lack of predictability and control in the situation quite apart from the element of injury".

When a trained investigator analyses a near-miss, he discovers why the injury or environmental damage *did not* occur...he understands why the individual involved is still alive. Indeed, there is often as much benefit in analysing the methods of error recovery as in analysing the means to avoid the error altogether (Fuller 1990: Habberley et al 1986). Proper and timely analysis therefore reveals how people are detecting and correcting things in practice (van der Schaaf & Kanse 2000); critical information for any system. By way of our understanding of 'common cause' then, information from properly gathered, grouped and analysed accidents can be used to assist future tasks and processes (Wright & van der Schaaf 2005). Of course, any investigation and analysis seeking to do this must have a well informed and objective view of cause.

In addition to Heinrich's key message being missed, there is a great deal of confusion surrounding his triangle in particular and accident severity/frequency data in general. His triangle makes no statement about the causes of accidents; that statement is made by his accident causation theory. Similarly then, there is no connection or relationship between the 'common cause hypothesis' and injury severity/frequency data (a point we will return to shortly when discussing multiple causation theory). Other than the key message, Heinrich's ratios do not apply to industry in general or to any organisation in particular; to assume such would smack of naivety. If an organisation wishes to construct such a triangle then it can only do so from its own data. Even then, the resulting information cannot provide any predictive capability as regards the relative timing or numbers of severe outcome accidents that might occur in the future. In addition, data analysts looking for causes must remain conscious of the fact that minor-injury accidents are often self-reported and/or not too deeply investigated at all. More serious outcome accidents, on the other hand, tend to be both reported and investigated in progressively more detail. Consequently, this is but one reason why two otherwise causally identical accidents can seem vastly different; another reason, of course, is confirmation bias.

Appropriately addressing near-miss and minor outcome accidents *will* bring about a reduction in the number of severe outcome accidents (Heinrich 1941: TYS). But, such reductions are highly unlikely ever to be directly proportional to one another. Not least, chance, the "scourge of accident research" (HSE 1998:43), plays a part that generally gathered statistics do not highlight unless the compiler of the data makes a clear cut statement to emphasise it. Consequently, and for instance, an organisation might show a reduction in overall numbers of fatal and minor-injury accidents only to suffer three fatalities in quick succession at the start of the very next reporting period (Beyer 1916: TYS). Such triangles and national statistics (e.g. RIDDOR in the UK or OSHA or the National Safety Council in the USA) therefore provide a retrospective report on what *has* happened, not a predictive report on what *will* or *might* happen.

Fact gives way to Fiction - the Emergence of the Management Failure School

Without doubt, Heinrich's Theory has stood the test of time (Heinrich 1959: Petersen 1971 & 1978: Bird 1974: Bird & Loftus 1976). Regardless of how many permutations or scenarios are imagined, the theory holds water. Nonetheless, and despite the fact that it had been widely and heavily supported, a small group opted to move away from it around the time of the 1970 Occupational, Safety and Health Act in America. According to Petersen (1971:13; 1978:16), this move occurred even though there was *"certainly nothing wrong"* with Heinrich's theory. His view, shared by many, was that Heinrich's text on accident prevention had given safety a much needed and well organised framework around which it could finally work. Similarly, Bird (1974:20) and Bird & Loftus (1976:39) said that it had been a classic in safety thinking and teaching for over 30 years.

For Bird (1974:20) and Bird & Loftus (1976:39), the move away was attributed to a perceived need to update (re-label) the dominoes to...

'reflect the direct management relationship involved with the causes of **all** *incidents that could downgrade a business operation'*.

However, nothing was offered by way of support for this 'new found' belief that management were now causatively involved in all accidents (consequently, we shall look closer at Bird's 'sequence' in Chapter Five). Returning to Petersen (1971:13; 1978), he further expressed the view that the move away was due to the safety profession having interpreted Heinrich's theory too narrowly. But, the wider interpretation being proposed by Petersen (1971:15) would come by way of 'multiple causation theory' (discussed shortly below) and the notion that "weaknesses in the management system" (i.e. management or organisational failures) were the "root causes" of *all* accidents.

An Erroneous Rejection of the Common Cause Hypothesis

Prior to the TYS, multiple causation theory in the context here had never been effectively, if ever, challenged. Furthermore, the theory is compelled to reject the 'common cause hypothesis'; but, it has no ground to do that (Difford 1998). For Difford, the first hint of there being something 'worryingly amiss' with multiple causation theory should have come by way of Petersen's (1971:16-17) query regarding the estimated data in Heinrich's triangle (recall Fig.ht. above and the brief discussion concerning it). Petersen says that whilst later studies had subsequently confirmed the generality of Heinrich's triangle, they had produced "completely different numbers". However, as with many writers and safety practitioners today, Petersen was under the impression that the ratios in Heinrich's triangle would be the same in any organisation or trade, irrespective of the work and risks involved. But, clear from the discussion earlier above, that impression expresses a considerable misunderstanding. No two studies (see Fig.bp. below) would be expected to produce the same figures in their triangles (see HSE (1997b) and five studies that *all* produced different figures).

Other writers have also expressed confusion about the triangles. For instance, Reason (2004:120) is under the impression that they represent the "iceberg theories of accident causation". Of course, there are no such theories and some might consider that statement to be a little odd to say the very least.

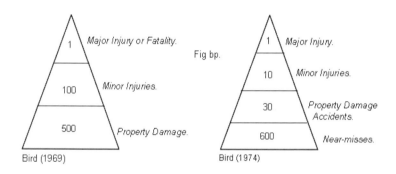

Nonetheless, with his (i.e. Petersen's) error undetected, Petersen (1971: 1978) moves on to discuss some accident severity and frequency data from the National Safety Council of America for the period 1926 to 1967. There, he notes a reported reduction of 80% in frequency rates across the USA compared to 'only' a 63% reduction in severity rates. Erroneously, if not a little naively perhaps, he argues that if the common cause hypothesis were correct, those percentages would mirror one another (i.e. they would fall in direct proportion to one another). On the basis that the percentages did not show a directly proportional fall, he argues that the causes of severe injury accidents must obviously be different to the causes of minor-injury accidents. By default, he is therefore also compelled to argue that the causes of near-miss accidents are different as well; something that is contrary, at the most rudimentary level, even to the examples of the bloody nose etc given earlier above (also see Lander et al 2010 and Bird 1974:18).

Of course, in addition to Petersen clearly rejecting the common cause hypothesis (see Wright & van der Schaaf 2004), he is also rejecting the value of near-miss and minor-injury investigations. Effectively, he is stating that their analysis would tell us nothing about the cause of more severe injury accidents. Transposing that view, he also believes that analysis of severe injury accidents can give us no preventative insight into the causes of less severe injury accidents either.

Clearly, Petersen's logic leaves much to be desired and his rejection of the common cause hypothesis was, without doubt, a mistake. Furthermore, it is contrary to findings in the field and numerous studies (e.g. TYS Construction & Engineering: Schmidt et al 2000 US Navy: Wright & van der Schaaf 2004 UK Railway). He has disregarded the many variables that exist to confound such statistics; not least, the role of chance (*R* v *Howe*). He appears also to be unaware of the difference between an accident and an injury (recall that the latter is the result of the former). Consequently, he was focussed on severity (as are many today) at the expense of the common cause hypothesis and, therefore, the value of near-miss and minor-injury data (of which there is far more) is lost.

In essence, Petersen's philosophy (shared by many, e.g. Swuste 2007; HSE 2003d; Manuele 2011:59) is that the cause of a man loosing his grip on a chain-saw will vary according to the injury that results; i.e. in similar circumstances, *the cause of a loss of grip* that results in a minor leg injury will be different to *the cause of a loss of grip* that results in a leg being cut to the bone. However, and the need for Personal Protective Equipment such as armoured trousers aside, the amount of energy released (i.e. transferred from the chainsaw to the leg) has no bearing whatsoever on the cause of the accident itself. If an engineer accidentally drills through the air receiver of a compressor and the receiver is empty, nothing results. However, if the air receiver is full then the energy released could have numerous different consequences; but, those consequences have no bearing at all on the cause of the accident; i.e. on the cause of him drilling through the air receiver in the first place.

As an alternative example to the above, consider the following; a man slips on a patch of cooking oil that has been spilt and not cleaned up in a kitchen where he works. According to Williams (2010), there will be just one root or proximate cause of this but, a multitude of possible effects or outcomes; for instance...

- The man slips and regains his balance without either injury or loss;

- The man slips and pulls a muscle in his groin but does not fall;

- The man slips and falls but occasions no injury;

- The man slips and falls, injuring his elbow;

- The man slips and falls and fractures his collar bone;

- The man slips and collides with a kitchen appliance knocking himself unconscious;

- The man slips and falls onto a lit stove. He is burnt by flames and scalded by boiling water;

- The man slips and falls onto a pan of boiling oil. The oil ignites but the fire is quickly extinguished;

- The man slips and falls onto a pan of boiling oil. The oil ignites and the kitchen is destroyed by fire;

- The man slips and falls onto a pan of boiling oil. The oil ignites and the kitchen is destroyed along with the building housing it and the property next door;

Clearly, analysis will reveal a behavioural cause (i.e. the common cause) of the slip in each instance. Nonetheless, according to multiple causation theory (to which we will now turn), the cause of the slip will vary according to which one of the ten possible outcomes listed above actually results. What's more, it claims that there will be numerous causes of the slip itself (by default, different on every occasion), all stemming from management or organisational failures.

A General Industrial Theory of Multiple Causation- Fact or Fiction?

According to Petersen (1971:13)...

> "...we know that behind every accident there lie many contributing factors, causes and subcauses. The theory of multiple causation is that these factors combine together in random fashion, causing accidents. If this is true, our investigation of accidents ought to identify some of these factors - as many as possible...".

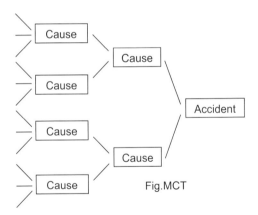

Fig.MCT

The first thing to note regarding the above statement is that it bases the theory of multiple causation on an apparently *known fact*; i.e. that *all* accidents have multiple causes. Whilst that statement is true, we will see that it is a truth only insofar as it relates, in error and confusion, to the antecedent causal chain as opposed to the chain of causes that are properly over-lapping or transitive (for example, imagine that a man on a beach has been sunburned. According to multiple causation theory, the underlying or proximate cause of the sunburn could be cited as being due to the sun having risen and/or the local council allowing people onto its beach. However, these are factors in the antecedent causal chain and we work through (or ignore) such 'causes' until we reach the deliberate act. Consequently, we find the proximate cause of the sunburn here to be the deliberate act of failing to apply sun screen).

Some theories (e.g. Reason's (1997) Swiss cheese model) will put it another way and suggest that the *known fact* is that multiple barriers or defences must fail before an accident can occur; however, how you view things (i.e. multiple causes or multiple failed barriers) makes no difference since such theories are indistinguishable. As a result, and whilst a *single* example to the contrary would be enough (or, for the academically inclined, we need *but one* of Popper's *Black Swans*), if a reasonable sampling of accidents reveals that they do not all involve multiple causes or failed barriers then such theories fall at the first hurdle and are disproved.

The second point of note relates to Petersen's use of the words *"if this is true"* in the above statement. That reminds us that the theory is nothing more than an assumption and that it is awaiting to be disproved; of course, some 'theories' should never be put forward in the first place. Causal models are, then, works in progress and should be constantly evaluated and re-evaluated (O'Brien et al 2004). Their authors should be monitoring for problems and alert to criticisms or contrary research that might suggest that the theory is wrong or needs formally withdrawing. Theories are supposed to assist such things as analysis, understanding, explanation and prediction. If they are wrong or turn out not to have any scientific basis, especially in a field such as ours where men's lives and the environment are at stake, they do more harm than good (Nemeth 2008).

Whilst Petersen's rejection of the common cause hypothesis was unwarranted, it was also rather fortuitous. The concept of cause and effect as a predictable and definable serial process is irreconcilable with multiple causation. Consequently, supporters (e.g. Hollnagel 2004) of multiple causation or Reason's Swiss Cheese model for instance are, whether they realise it or not, compelled to reject it. However, we will see that their unnecessarily wide and relentless pursuit of upstream factors (Young et al 2004:3) has left a 'serial killer' on the loose (Difford 2004). Petersen's statement also suggests that a well developed body of literature exists that has analysed multiple causation's main features and examined the implications for causal reasoning. However, no such body of literature exists and Petersen provided no evidence himself that might explain or support the assumption that the first part of the statement was *'known'* either. Similarly, actual, testable examples of what the multiple factors were in reality and how they had been found to combine together in random fashion to cause a reasonable sample of professionally analysed accidents were also absent. Instead, Petersen (1971:19-20) moved to introduce 5 basic principles of which 1 & 2 are relevant here;

(P1): "An unsafe act, an unsafe condition, an accident: all these are symptoms of something wrong in the management system".

(P2): "certain sets of circumstances can be predicted to produce severe injuries".

Principal 1., a massive assumption that can be considered hand in hand with the main premise, is categoric as regards a causal relationship between management and *all* accidents (in fact, we will see that it presents an invariable and unconditional statement of cause that simply cannot be met). However, in the scientific context, demonstrating a causal relationship is a matter of persuasion born of scientific method and careful data analysis (O'Brien et al 2004). Yet, despite the sweeping and conclusive nature of the principle, nothing was provided by way of real-time examples, observations or findings that might lend any type of support to it; which, given the way that the theory was, and remains to be, embraced is quite remarkable. Petersen's theory effectively rests on premise 1. (and vice versa) and some might have expected numerous examples in support. However, even in the second edition of the book (Petersen 1978) that introduced the theory, nothing further emerged. That said, many were not surprised (TYS). Certainly, numerous examples were not what was needed; Petersen needed to demonstrate *how* **all** accidents were caused, ultimately and categorically, by management. In addition, he would needed to have presented an extremely convincing and powerful argument in support of his belief that all causes are always transitive since experts in the field of causation had, and continue to, comprehensively argue and categorically rejected such notions (Hart & Honore 2002:43).

As for Principle number 2, that is a statement of undeniable fact that this book fully supports. However, as a statement made by multiple causation theory, it is simply a contradiction. How can a theory that has rejected the common cause hypothesis now state that "certain sets of circumstances can be predicted to produce severe injuries"? Petersen provides a considerable list of high risk activities and notes that a much longer list could easily be made. Consequently, he should have been able to provide numerous relevant examples in support. However, he does not describe how the unexplained, random and interrelated phenomena occur there either. Similarly, he fails to explain how the causes of these severe injury accidents are now, all of a sudden, identifiable in advance. Clarification was clearly needed since principle number 2. says something that multiple causation itself should not be able to say given that the two concepts (i.e. common cause and multiple cause) cannot co-exist.

The thrust of the 'modern' academic argument against common cause is that all accidents are unique; that is, authors such as Reason (1990:174) believe that "the same mixture of causes is unlikely to recur." However, many (Heinrich 1941: 1959: TYS and, not least, common sense) would disagree; preventable accidents are "predictable events with known causes and risk factors" (Christoffel & Gallagher 2006:89). If this were not the case then most preventionists would have gone home; what would be the point in addressing the cause of any accident if the next one was going to be completely different? what would be the point if the next, albeit 'identical', accident was going to have a completely new and unique set of multiple causes? The result would be an endless exercise of reactive fire fighting and tail chasing; which, as ludicrous as that sounds, is strangely familiar. As it happens, much of industry engages in this and the cause is directly traceable to the underlying philosophy of multiple causation (Difford 2004); indeed, its sole cause, as we shall see, is confusion amidst the academic community and their inability to differentiate between antecedent and transitive causes.

Perhaps multiple causation is 'just' a model and was never meant to be a theory at all. Certainly, D. A. Weaver produced a supporting 'model' of sorts by way of an extreme adjustment to a Heinrich type domino sequence and Petersen (1978:xiv) says that Weaver helped him to "develop many, perhaps most, of the ideas" in his book (we will look to Weaver's (1971) sequence later below). However, if multiple causation is not a theory then it cannot, contrary to some (Abdelhamid & Everett 2005), be a model either. In order for multiple causation to be a model it would need to be constructed around, or at least have reflected and discussed, the key elements of a particular theory; the fact that it does not is extremely problematic.

'All Roads Lead to Rome'

From just the eight italicised lines relating to Petersen at pages 22 & 24 above, the clear philosophy of multiple causation is that all accidents, unsafe acts, unsafe conditions, contributing factors, causes and sub-causes are management or system failures; what Petersen refers to elsewhere as 'underlying root causes'. Unfortunately, and devoid of either scientific or observational basis, a wholly unsubstantiated and incredibly biased view of causation commenced a management failure feeding frenzy that continues to this day. For instance, 16 years after Petersen, Grose (1987:12) would offer that...

*"Less obvious to the layman is the **idea** that nearly all accidental losses have **multiple** causes; virtually no accident has a single cause".*

26

Shortly thereafter, Ferry (1988:198: citing Bruggink) would highlight the following comments from Andrews and Pope respectively...

'Except for Acts of God, every accident, no matter how minor is a failure of the organization'.

'Accidents are only managerial excuses for operational errors that result from managerial failures'.

In the same text, by way of reference to Petersen (1978), Ferry (1988:199) asks his students to consider the following hypothesis;

"In the investigation of any mishap, there can always be found some degree of management involvement or activity that might in some way have prevented the mishap. Therefore it is arbitrarily assumed that management will be responsible for the causes of every mishap, and the existence of every hazard".

The words *'arbitrarily assumed'* in the above 'hypothesis' perhaps summarise the enormous problem that this book is intent on highlighting. Within the general industrial setting and the so-called 'high risk' or 'technologically complex' sectors, the causes of accidents (whether they involve health care, off-shore platforms or aviation for instance) are *not* being logically determined; they are being arbitrarily attributed by way of questionable 'theory'. Already noted, if the philosophies upon which they are based are flawed, then they are part of the problem...not the solution.

Ten years later came Reason's (1997:2004:11) Swiss cheese model (SCM) complete, amongst other things, with a familiar infection;

"the necessary condition for an organisational accident is the rare conjunction of a set of holes in successive defences"

We will look closer at the so-called organisational accident in Chapter Six. For now, it is enough to note that the SCM premise, reminiscent of Petersen's language, assumes that these sets of holes are "latent weaknesses in the system" and that accidents would not happen but for their existence (Reason et al 2006:20).

To save labouring things unnecessarily, we can conclude here with Raouf (1998) via the International Labour Organization (ILO)...

"multiple causation theory is an outgrowth of the domino theory....It postulates that for a single accident there may be many contributory factors, causes and sub-causes, and that certain combinations of these give rise to accidents. According to this theory, the contributory factors can be grouped into the following two categories:

Behavioural. This category includes factors pertaining to the worker, such as improper attitude, lack of knowledge, lack of skills and inadequate physical and mental condition.

Environmental. This category includes improper guarding of other hazardous work elements and degradation of equipment through use and unsafe procedures"...adding that...

'the major contribution of this theory is to bring out the fact that rarely, if ever, is an accident the result of a single cause or act".

Let's now apply the contrary context to Raouf's (1998) *behavioural* and *environmental* categories and assume that we have...

- A worker with a good attitude who possesses all of the necessary knowledge and skills and is in A1 physical and mental condition; who is in...

- An A1 environment that has proper guarding of all hazardous work elements and contains no degraded equipment and no unsafe procedures.

Let's assume that, tragically, this worker has died during a routine job in that workplace. Let's also assume no management failures and that all necessary legislative and system controls were in place.

In real terms, according to Popper (2002), a single accident such as the one above (i.e. a single exception to the rule) would disprove the above views of Andrews, Pope, Reason's (1997) SCM and Petersen's multiple causation theory at a stroke. But, multiple causation theory is not always cited in absolute terms; some writers have opted to slightly temper its otherwise concrete nature by installing qualifiers like... *'virtually no accident has a single cause*; or...*rarely if ever does an accident have a single cause'*. So, and whilst we do not need to temper anything, let's see how rare or nonexistent are the accidents that otherwise disprove the above statements, model and theory?

Deliberate Acts or Management Failures?

In the United States of America, Heinrich (1941:20) found that 88% of the accidents in his study had been caused by unsafe acts. Later, Bird and Germain (1966:44) would offer that 90% of all disabling injuries were caused by someone violating a known safety rule or practice. Of note, and whilst he later reduced that figure to 85%, Bird (1974:166) conceded that *"compliance with established rules would see a substantial reduction of major problems faced by management"*.

In Scotland, Her Majesty's Chief Inspector of Factories (J.D. Hammer) studied 100 consecutive, fatal accidents occurring in the construction sector between 1969 and 1975. Whilst he said that it was "not easy to apportion responsibility" for any of the deaths, he decided that 18 were attributable to the deceased, 2 to a co-worker and that 12 others could not be assigned to any party (HSE 1978:17). Regarding 9 of the deaths in particular, Hammer cited the cause as being due to the deceased working contrary to instruction and in 'acceptance' of clear risk. Of note here, in an unrelated study, workers were asked who they thought was best placed to reduce the chance of them having an accident; 1) Themselves, 2) Other workers, 3) Supervisors or 4) Management & Unions. In response, 70% felt that they *themselves* were best placed to avoid accidents with the next highest category of replies being *Other workers* (Hale & Perusse 1977 citing McKenna). In addition (to assist later), note from Hammer's study that it *is not* always possible to identify the proximate or 'root cause'. Consequently, on that point alone, how can management be causatively responsible for *all* accidents?

In an earlier UK study, a team of Factory Inspectors had kept 140 sites under surveillance for a period of six months. Of the 270 reportable accidents that occurred, 81% were found *not* to be due to clear breaches of legislation. Of note, the Inspectors reported that additional regulations would not have helped. (Robens Report. Cmnd. 5034:8).

Across other parts of the UK, a report into 739 construction fatalities that occurred between 1981 and 1985 led the Director General of the Health and Safety Executive (HSE) to offer that, in 70% of cases, positive action by management could have saved lives (HSE 1988) (according to Williams (2010), the only way that such a figure can be arrived at is by way of comparison to prosecution 'successes'). In HSE (1986), a report into 296 deaths that occurred in the agricultural sector between 1981 and 1984, it was concluded that management were *not* responsible for 38% of the deaths. In a later study entitled 'A Deadly Maintenance' (HSE 1985), the percentage of deaths that were *not* attributable to management was 46%.

In Free's (1994) study of railway accidents it was concluded that "almost every accident involved an error in conjunction with a violation" (HSE 1998:34).

The UK Health & Safety Executive (HSE) acknowledge that accidents can occur despite suitable and sufficient risk assessments having been made *and* appropriate preventive and protective measures being taken (HSE 2007:16); but, their view is that the fundamental causes are "usually" rooted deeper in management (HSE 2003a:4) (clearly, the first part of that statement disproves the management failure myth and renders the second part to be incomprehensible nonsense). However, the word 'usually' does not seem to be in keeping with, for instance, the finding in 'A Deadly Maintenance' that 46% of the deaths *were not* attributable to management. Similarly, it is clear from the HSE's Director General that 30% of the 739 deaths to which he refers *could not possibly* have been rooted deeper in management; in fact, the HSE's view is simply contrary to its own data analysis and, on many occasions, the views of the Courts as well.

According to Williams (2010), the prosecution success rate in the UK has been relatively stable at 70% throughout the period of the IIAI's first Ten Year Study; i.e. the Crown wins about two out of every three cases (or, loses one in three depending on your view point). However, he asks whether the word 'success' is appropriate given that during the 2009/2010 period, around 90% of prosecution 'successes' came by way of guilty pleas (before certain readers get excited, there is more on this later below). On the other hand, in defended cases, the Crown lost on about 94% of occasions. Even though the prosecution does not have to prove cause (*R* v *Chargot*), the Courts are regularly returning verdicts that question both the findings of regulatory investigations and the decisions to prosecute.

The HSE view that management failures are usually the root causes of accidents is also out of step with many of the research reports that it has commissioned. For instance, in HSE (2002), regarding the off-shore industries, it was found that violations were linked to between 70% and 90% of accidents. In HSE (2004a), it was found that problems stemmed more from the violation of known rules than from any lack of knowledge. In HSE (2004b), it was said that violations were common, even if method statements etc are fully disseminated. In HSE (2004c) it was stated that, whilst the risk from work at height is repeatedly recognised, progress in reducing accidents is hampered by those who know and comprehend best practice but fail to apply it. That report, as did Bird (1974), felt that most accidents could be avoided if individuals would follow the procedures that were laid down to protect them; in keeping with which, HSE (2004b) found that workers at height, when caught without being clipped on, tended not to argue that they were unaware of the requirement.

On the wider European front, Article 5(4) of Directive 89/391/EEC allows a member state to exclude or limit liability where occurrences are due to unforeseeable circumstances that are beyond the employer's control; i.e. where the consequences could not have been avoided despite the exercise of all due care. Similarly, the Civil Courts have long reminded us that there is such a thing as the 'pure accident'; i.e. the accident that occurs despite the relevant duty holder having taken all due care (*Donoghue* v *Stephenson*).

In Australia, over a three year period in the early 1980s, Feyer & Williamson (1998) found that behavioural factors were involved in 90% of fatal accidents.

Finally, returning to the common cause issue discussed earlier, Wright & van der Schaaf (2004) reference a study by Williamson et al (1996) which concluded a common cause for all of the deaths involved. In addition, to assist later when we consider Bird's (1974) management failure model, it can be noted here that Bird (1974:18) believes that the causes of all incidents "are usually the same". However, if the reader goes through this section again and keeps the opening comments by Bird & Germain and Bird in mind, it should be clear that the management failure school philosophy is based almost exclusively on the belief that a man is never the cause of his own behaviour; i.e. that a man is never responsible for his own actions.

Self-supervision

Whilst it may be true to say that an unsafe act might not have occurred had the relevant individual been under supervision at a particular time, it is also true that supervision would be largely unnecessary if employees followed the rules and instructions laid down to protect them (Lateiner & Heinrich 1969:109; Bird 1974: HSE 2004c). That said, supervision is a legal requirement in most jurisdictions; however, and in the vast majority of cases, neither the courts, regulators nor competent people expect supervision to be constant. In reality, levels of supervision are, therefore, determined according to the risks and competencies involved. Consequently, following such determinations, the majority of us are properly and legally entitled to work unsupervised for relatively lengthy periods of time; that is, we are allowed to work under our own "self-supervision" (HSE 2003b:21). As Lord Pearce said in *ICI* v *Shatwell*...

"The employers had striven without compromise to prevent shot-firers testing in the open. They had done everything that they could to enforce the safety rules. They had been influential in tightening up the regulations imposed on the shot-firers personally, they had publicly punished and degraded a shot-firer who tested in the open, and they had in consequence faced trouble with the Union. They had arranged a system of work and pay designed to discourage the cutting of time and the taking of risks. The two shot-firers...knew all this. In spite of it they deliberately broke the statutory regulations which were laid on them personally and together tested in the open. As a result they blew themselves up. They were trained, trusted, certificated men and it would have been absurd to have someone to watch over them."

INTERIM SUMMARY

Prior to the Ten Year Study undertaken by Neucom Ltd for the Institute of Industrial Accident Investigators, Heinrich's (1931) was the most modern of its kind. However, his principle findings (for purposes here) were, quite simply, that 88% of the accidents in his study were caused by 'unsafe acts' of persons and 10% by 'unsafe conditions'; that said, we will shortly see why Heinrich's distinction between unsafe acts and unsafe conditions was slightly misleading since unsafe conditions can result only from unsafe acts.

Of course, the exact form or nature of any unsafe act or omission will vary from accident to accident. But, the common cause itself in any accident will always be one of human behaviour and this is a tragic fact irrespective of whether the particular act occurred in the instant time frame or prior to it.

Obviously, the finding of a common cause runs counter to notions of multiple causation. Nonetheless, Petersen's (1971) rejection of it was erroneous. Similarly, his belief that unsafe acts, etc are but symptoms of something wrong in the system was, and still is, contrary to fact. There is no basis for Petersen's (or the UK HSE's for instance) belief that the causes of accidents are rooted in management or systems ...none at all; indeed, it should be obvious that complete compliance with the law does not prevent accidents. Multiple so-called contributing factors, causes and sub-causes do not lie causatively behind every accident; that is a myth. The myth requires that the numerous factors in the antecedent causal chain are always viewed as being transitive and it also requires belief in an exceptionless (invariable and unconditional) causal statement that is false. That said, the myth requires the employment of an arbitrary 'stop-rule' insofar as all investigations will halt (and start) at management. However, if all causes are always transitive then there is absolutely no justifiable reason whatsoever to ever end the causal search at management; logically, there will always be a cause beyond it.

At this point, and on empirical data alone, multiple causation theory is disproved. Of course, it should have been disproved upon its very release; nonetheless, a veritable management failure feeding frenzy took place around it that continues, illogically and insupportably, to this very day.

Inventions such as multiple causation theory assist neither analysis, understanding, explanation nor prediction...they block it. Unchallenged, they support those such as Reason (1990) who believe that "the same mixture of causes is unlikely to recur." Whilst that is the voice of inexperience expressing its ignorance of the need for causes to be transitive rather than merely antecedent, it effectively reduces the accident phenomenon to the realm of the unpredictable; consequently, to the unpreventable. That said, and hopefully, the cause of industry's relentless and reactive fire-fighting should now be a little more obvious.

As regards their causes, accidents are not multifactorially unique; they are singularly common. Indeed, those that are preventable are highly amenable to prediction by the properly trained. Nonetheless, later (e.g. Bird 1974) and more modern writers (e.g. Reason 1997) would support the following as referred to earlier by Ferry (1988)...

"In the investigation of any mishap, there can always be found some degree of management involvement or activity that might in some way have prevented the mishap".

Apart, as we shall see, from that statement being a clear indication that its originator had no understanding of how or why the chain of causal antecedents is cut short, it expresses an absence of awareness regarding the critical distinctions that exist between causes and conditions; to which we shall now, amongst other things, turn.

Chapter Two Part 1:
Distinguishing Causes from Conditions

Root Cause: A System Term – A System Test

Petersen (1971: 1978:18) appeared to be aware of the essence of a system compliant description of a root cause since he says that *"root causes are those whose correction would effect permanent results"*. However, (and relying in part on Difford' (2004) analysis of total quality management and the relevant ISO (9001) standard), the root cause being put forward should...

- be *the cause*, logically and demonstrable, of the effect or problem in question; and

- be under the direct control of the system.

As regards the remedy or correction proposed, this should...

- be arrived at having considered any and all other options;

- remove the problem and prevent it from recurring; and, importantly...

- its effect should be determined *before* any decision to interfere with the relevant system or process is made.

Even in the raw form presented here, the above points will be familiar to any system manager. Not least, they will be recognised and generally accepted by any organisation with a Quality Assurance program, especially one certified to ISO 9000. Yet, supporters of multiple causation and Reason's (1997) SCM for instance consider the term root cause to be "fallacious"; according to Hollnagel (2004:53), *"analysis can always be taken one or more steps further back"* (if so, and once again, why stop at management?). However, Professor Hollnagel is wrong; causal analysis *cannot* always be taken one or more steps further back (Hart & Honore 2002). Indeed, as we shall see, that all too common and erroneous practice, whereby cause is arbitrarily and persistently relocated upstream, expresses a confused notion of cause within any who would promote it (according to the TYS, HSG245's (HSE 2004d) view is amongst the most confused).

Petersen's causal language is also confused. Whilst he commits the basic error of using the terms root cause and underlying cause as if interchangeable (OHSAS 18002:2008, for instance, also does this), he also uses them in combination; e.g. discussing his 'symptoms', Petersen (1978:26) says that they have systemic *"underlying root causes"*. Unfortunately, that confusion has wider ramifications.

From the earlier discussion regarding Petersen's premise and his principle number one, we know that 'symptoms' include contributing factors, causes, sub-causes, *unsafe acts* and *conditions*. However, he says that whilst these may be the immediate cause of an accident, they are *"invariably...not the root cause"*. Consequently (and ignoring the fact that a condition cannot possibly be a cause), that statement *alone* 'allows' multiple causation theory to move beyond an unsafe or deliberate act in the belief that its cause (i.e. the cause of a cause) will, *without exception,* reside upstream with management. However, and not surprisingly, there is an absence of discussion regarding *how* the numerous (if not infinite) 'symptoms' of management failure assumed by multiple causation theory are determined; this, so as to justify their new found status as root causes beyond the clear fact that they are simply assumed from the outset. Similarly, reference to tests such as the one introduced at the start of this section (or to the contrasts (discussed shortly below) that are critical if we are not to confuse causes with *conditions*) are also (ominously perhaps) absent. Whilst they clearly ignore Ockham's warning that *plurality must never be posited without necessity,* supporters of multiple causation seem to forget that each of their so-called causes would need to be analysed separately (Lombroso 1911) and then weighed, one against the other (Honore 2010).

As it is, all of the terms available to multiple causation (unsafe act, unsafe condition, contributing factor, cause, sub-cause and underlying cause) are ultimately destined to be reinterpreted (or, more correctly, misinterpreted) and ***arbitrarily*** re-labelled as root causes. However, if you assume that management failures cause all accidents and that anything and everything is but a symptom of this, assumption and terminology reduces your investigation to a self-fulfilling prophecy. Worse still, with neither mechanism nor attention regarding how the root cause has been identified (let alone confirmed), it is more probable than not that the resulting remedial intervention strategy will be ineffective if not counter-productive; furthermore and naturally, *the cause* and the potential for loss will still be in place.

As for causal terminology in general, the TYS found a confusion of language in many of the accident reports that it surveyed; problems that were common regardless of jurisdiction or sector. Critical terms were not properly defined, if defined at all, in many of the associated systems that used them. Where they were 'defined', the definition was usually that of the relevant regulator as transferred into the business by its safety advisors. Regardless of the origin of the definition, when individuals from the same organisations were asked to define key terms that their businesses used, they were either unable to or, would provide varyingly dissimilar and/or inaccurate definitions. Indeed, in relation to the terms 'immediate' and 'underlying' cause within the UK for instance, HSE (2001:iii) found that the majority of companies surveyed had failed to effectively discriminate or understand the distinction between them; upon which, we might conclude here by way of reference to the following from the UK Hazardous Installations Directorate…

"…underlying causes may be judged differently by various parties and it may often prove difficult to establish a unanimous opinion in the course of an accident investigation. For example,

an incident which is ostensibly caused by operative error may have a deeper cause in such shortcomings as poor training, lack of supervision, failure of management to provide reasonable safeguards against human error, etc. Underlying causes thus normally need to be resolved in a court of law" (HSE 2003c).

Regulatory Breaches & System Non-conformances – Causes or Incidental Facts?

Depending on the construction of an offence, the criminal law is sometimes compelled to convict in cases where the defendant's behaviour would not be deemed causative according to commonsense and logic. For instance, in *R v Williams [2010]*, a case arising from the death of a pedestrian who had stepped out in front of a passing car, the defendant driver was convicted of *"causing death by driving without insurance and without a license"*. The conviction was upheld by the Court of Appeal even though that Court acknowledged that *"no fault, carelessness or lack of consideration in driving"* could be attributed to the defendant; indeed, the death was accepted as being due solely to the victim's own fault to such an extent that civil action (where causation is required) would not be an option in view of the findings. Such convictions, difficult but necessary, arise via **strict liability** offences; that is, no fault or negligence of any sort is required of a defendant or duty holder (also see *Empress Car Co*).

From what has been discussed so far, it is clear that the UK HSE and writers such as Petersen are effectively attempting to attach strict liability to organisations via their default belief that management are the root cause of virtually all accidents. Unfortunately, by way of official publications and the general position of health & safety bodies world-wide, many have unwittingly succumbed to this highly illogical, erroneous and improper philosophy. Worse still, flat-lined accident statistics Worldwide (TYS) do not appear to have suggested to them that their remedial intervention strategies may be wrong.

The relevant area of the TYS identified a tendency in those who would 'adopt' the role of investigator (not least, safety practitioners) to embark on an automatic hunt for regulatory breaches and system non-conformances (a hunt, equating to little more than a post-accident audit or inspection, that was sometimes akin to a witch hunt: TYS). The tendency was driven by a firmly held belief that most, if not all, accidents are caused by multiple management failures and that these exist exclusively as regulatory breaches and/or system non-conformances. But, when asked to explain the process that they had utilised to arrive at the finding of cause, most were unable to do so.

In jurisdictions where applicable laws existed, the default tendency was to cite a lack of compliance with an associated piece of legislation (often, the 'link' to the legislation being cited required a considerable leap of faith if not a bizarre stretch of the imagination) (of note, the TYS found an alarming absence of 'system-speak' amongst those who should have been far more familiar with management system requirements). However, objective re-analysis of the vast majority of causes put forward during investigations that were physically monitored by the TYS found them *not to be causes* at all. A similar trend, although not immediately obvious to the untrained eye since reports tend to conceal their assumptions, was also found in accident reports that the TYS only reviewed. In the majority of cases, the investigators agreed that what they had originally identified as causes were, in fact, *'mere conditions' or 'incidental facts'*. That is, even though attention to the things that they had (albeit erroneously) identified as causes might be necessary and correct if they were conducting an audit or inspection perhaps, they subsequently agreed that the attention or remedy that they were recommending would still have left *the cause* unaddressed.

That said, the problems confronting industry, its safety advisors and investigators is not founded in their inability to identify causes; on the contrary, the problem resides in the inability to recognise things that are *not causes*. As 'Sherlock Holmes' put it when explaining the form of erroneous reasoning known as the 'Digby effect'...

"It is of the highest importance in the art of detection to be able to recognize, out of a number of facts, which are incidental and which vital" (Sir Arthur Conan Doyle).

Of course, and assuming that it is within the investigator's scope of work, suspected breaches and/or system non-conformances should be appropriately identified to the relevant party or duty holder. However, safety practitioners in particular should check any tendency to cite these as causes. Firstly, we know that systems have their own tests; tests that are scientifically driven and sufficiently precise. Secondly, the belief in management failures as causes is *not theirs*, it has been programmed in by regulators and certain training providers contrary to the available factual evidence (TYS); as Swuste (2008) notes, there is little to show that either management systems or organisational characteristics are directly linked to safe performance.

In the UK for instance, researchers could not answer the question *"what would rates of workplace injury be in the absence of the HSE?"* (HSE 2005:104). The inability to answer such a question lies in one fact...there is no empirical evidence to support the widely held belief that compliance with the law and/or regulatory codes etc are reducing, let alone preventing, accidents (TYS). Indeed, Difford (2004) believes that health & safety management and accident prevention *are not* one and the same thing. Furthermore, he offers that accident prevention and regulatory compliance *are not* one and the same thing either (a view shared, oddly perhaps, by Petersen (1978:xiv) in the USA for example). Consequently, the average safety practitioners' belief (and many others: TYS) that criminal responsibility readily attaches to the organisation by way of the 'causes' that they (often casually) put forward is also without basis.

Fault sufficient only to attach the offence does not automatically provide proof that the offence *actually caused* the result (Smith & Hogan 1999:42); according to Difford (2004), in the context here for offences that attach to organisations, it "never does". Consequently, industry should be alert to the possibility that its in-house investigators could be unwittingly mirroring the regulatory investigation; indeed, many in-house investigators *are* doing that (TYS). Already noted, prosecutors in the UK and similar jurisdictions do not have to prove that the breach caused the result (*Chargot*). In fact, UK regulatory investigations (always conducted with prosecution in mind) are unlikely ever to be concerned with either cause, prevention or factors that might exonerate a defendant. To highlight this, Williams (2011) draws attention to the Code of Practice made under the UK's Criminal Procedure and Investigations Act 1996. That Act requires Health & Safety Executive and Local Authority (LA) investigators to have "*regard*" to any relevant provision of the Code. One such provision is that the investigator "*should pursue all reasonable lines of enquiry, whether these point towards or away from the suspect*"; however, the Health & Safety Executive (HSE) responded to that as follows...

"*Implicit in this phrase is the requirement that investigators should pursue lines of enquiry that could assist the defence. This is clearly a move away from the normal investigation process in which the investigator primarily looks for evidence to support the prosecution case. It requires the investigator to be a "finder of fact".*" (HSE W1).

According to the TYS, there is no evidence at present to suggest that HSE or LA investigations are doing anything more than have '*regard*' to the requirement. However, and more importantly here perhaps, the TYS found that most in-house investigators (especially, once again, those whose normal role is the provision of safety advice) also tended to ignore facts that were inconsistent with their default view of cause; unfortunately, that was found to have further negative effects where criminal action had resulted.

The TYS found that most Organisations that successfully defend alleged breaches of industrial safety law tend to do nothing. For them, further analysis is deemed unnecessary since the Courts have apparently upheld their 'belief' that all was well. On the other hand, convicted Organisations tended only to address the breach (as unspecific and general as that often is). For them, further analysis is also deemed unnecessary since their belief (widely held but mistaken) is that attention to the breach will automatically attend to the cause of the accident as well.

Either way, the organisation should require its investigator to make a clear statement regarding the cause of the accident irrespective of the cause of the regulatory breach since the two are unlikely to be addressed by the same remedial intervention strategy. If the in-house investigation has not demonstrably confirmed the breach to be *the cause* of the accident then, as necessary as it will be to address the breach, the cause must be assumed to be still in place. Similarly, for those who successfully defend themselves, doing nothing also leaves the cause in place. Regardless of the fact that there was no breach, there was still an accident. Consequently, the business should require the investigator (since it has a moral obligation to both employees and stake-holders) to state clearly what did cause the accident since, whatever it was, it has and is still able to, by-pass the system.

Causes or Mere Conditions?

The historical debate surrounding cause and effect has raged pre-Aristotle (322 bc-384 bc). Since then, a vast body of literature has been generated such as that by, and subsequent to, writers such as Galileo, Kant, Hume, Mill and Mackie; to name just a few. Even a statement like "*a cause marks a difference between the situation where the effect occurs and a contrasting situation where it does not*" (Lipton 1992:10) is not, whilst considered perfectly correct here, safe from analysis. That statement alone prompted discussion on how such a contrast might be chosen and on how highly context sensitive *causal selection* is (Broadbent 2008). Of course, as with the brief discussion earlier on the causes of criminal behaviour, schools of thought are many and varied. Consequently, with causal analysis and prevention in mind (not notions of blame or punishment in either the civil or criminal contexts), we will proceed with a logical and commonsense view of cause as derived from the eminent legal perspective of Hart & Honore (2002). Before we do, let's briefly consider Broadbent's (2008) view that cause is in some way 'selected'.

Such a view, shared by those (e.g. Dekker 2002: Hollnagel 2004 citing Woods et al 1994) who believe that cause is 'constructed', is incorrect. We do not 'select', from amongst a set of conditions, the one that we treat as cause (Hart & Honore 2002:31); the belief that all conditions, necessary or otherwise, have an equal right to be labelled as causes is wrong (Hart & Honore 2002:21). Causes are found and it is only when the critical contrasts between them and mere conditions are understood that the latter is prevented from clouding the former. To get us going then, Hart & Honore's (2002:34) general contrast between a *cause* and a *mere condition* can be summarised as follows;

- Mere conditions are factors that, whilst present when the accident happens, are also present when the accident does not happen.

- Even if it can be said that the accident would not have occurred had the 'mere condition' not been there, it is still rejected as the cause.

- To cite factors that are present during both the accident and the 'normal functioning' explain nothing; such factors do not 'make the difference'.

By way of a purely fictitious example; imagine a man walking along his local High Street. For reasons known only to himself, he walks into a lamp post...a lamp-post he has successfully negotiated hundreds of times before...not to mention all of the other lamp-posts that he has also avoided. So, what is the cause of this accident? True, "but-for" the lamp-post, that accident would not have happened. But, the question is not enquiring about things that would have *prevented* the collision, the question relates to what *caused* it! So, is the lamp-post the cause, or a mere condition?

Whilst pedestrians *do* collide with lamp-posts (in the same way that they collide with each other, telephone kiosks and waste paper bins for instance) they do not 'usually' or 'normally' collide with them. More importantly, unless in the process of falling down for instance, lamp-posts *never* collide with pedestrians; lamp-posts must be acted upon. Therefore, we immediately reject the lamp-post as being the cause of the accident since it is present when the accident happens and, it is also present when the accident does not happen (i.e. it is a condition); in the circumstances here, it cannot be a cause of an accident. Consequently, the focus of attention would not stray far from the man; or, more correctly, from the *deliberate act* (Hart & Honore 2002).

Whilst his act was neither voluntary nor intentional in the literal sense, his collision is 'unusual' or 'abnormal' and it is therefore *he* who has *'made the difference'* (i.e. been the cause) on this occasion.

For now, that rather simplistic explanation will suffice to commence the highlighting of the contrasts between causes and conditions that are "an inseparable feature of all causal thinking" (Hart & Honore 2002:12). Of course, cause should not be oversimplified; but, it should not be overcomplicated either (*R* v *Williams*). Either way, there is nothing mysterious about it and its essence is not affected by the apparent complexity or criticality of the problem under the spotlight.

Commonsense Analysis of Cause in R v Williams

Whilst the findings of the courts were proper under the circumstances there, let's see if the cited causes were causative of the *Williams'* accident for purposes here.

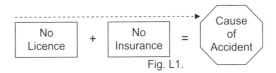

Fig. L1.

Effectively, an investigator would be stating that the absence of a driving licence and insurance was the cause of the accident (Fig.L1). That said, according to the construction of the relevant section of the Road Traffic Act 1988, the defendant would also have been judged to have caused the accident even if he had been in possession of one or the other (Fig.L2 & FigL3).

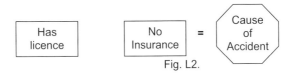

Fig. L2.

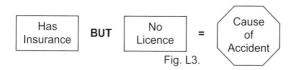

Fig. L3.

As regards a goal of future prevention for instance, the investigator is effectively claiming that someone who holds insurance and a licence will not have an accident (Fig.L4).

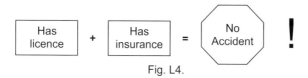

Fig. L4.

But, analysis of relevant data reveals that hundreds of thousands of vehicle accidents each year involve drivers who *do* possess licences and insurance (Fig.L5). In addition, it is clear that drivers who are not in possession of licences and insurance are not, necessarily, any more likely to have accidents than those who are; certainly, as in Williams' case, when their driving skills are not in question (that said, the courts (*Nettleship* v *Weston*) expect the same standard of *care* from novice drivers as they do from skilled ones). Consequently, the absence of a licence and insurance cannot be said to have been the cause of this accident; attention has been paid to causatively irrelevant matters.

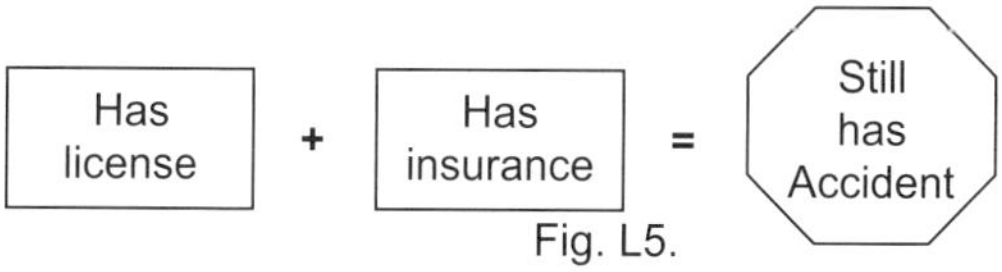

Has license	+	Has insurance	=	Still has Accident

Fig. L5.

Notwithstanding the need to address the matter of licences and insurances in the everyday and industrial contexts, we can see how commonsense would reject such would-be causes (not that we should be focussed on these or mere conditions in the first place) before they misdirect resources and confuse preventative strategies. Clearly, the pedestrian 'made the difference' on this occasion; i.e. his 'unsafe act' in the face of an obvious danger or hazard was the 'immediate' cause of the accident. As a result of that realisation, tragic and difficult though it sometimes is, we now have information that is essential if *the* root, proximate or underlying cause (also of a personal nature) is ever to be properly identified, analysed and addressed.

Unfortunately, there are those who will *always* seek to relocate the proximate cause of any accident up-stream; i.e. back in time and far away from the relevant deliberate act (notwithstanding, as with the lamp-post collision, that the pedestrian's act was neither voluntary nor deliberate in the literal sense). However, the causes put forward by investigators and analysts are found, all too often, to be based on correlations or relationships that, upon re-analysis, turn out not to be causes at all (i.e. the assumed causal relationships are spurious). Of note, the TYS found this to be a consistent problem with investigations or analyses that had utilised, for instance, the models and philosophies of Petersen (1971), the UK HSE, Bird (1974) and Reason (1997:2004).

Risk-laden – Or Merely Normal?

For the objective and impartial industrial accident investigator, the term 'normal functioning' does not mean a perfect or risk free environment (Hart & Honore 2002:36); and neither does it have to (*R v Chargot: Commission of the EU v UK*). The term 'normal' or 'usual' must be applied in context to the reality of the events and circumstances in question; i.e. as they are usually, or entitled to be, found rather than how someone's subjective or self-interested opinion *thinks* they should be found. For instance, the High Street in the lamp-post accident above has to accommodate cyclists, motorists and pedestrians. Some pedestrians are parents with pushchairs to contend with whilst others are parents with children to contend with; indeed, some pedestrians will be very young whilst others will be very old. Some will be disabled and some will be blind. Some will have both hands occupied whilst others will be wielding things like umbrellas. Some will be using mobile phones whilst still walking and others will be gazing into shop windows (risking collisions with lamp-posts!) whilst still walking. Pedestrians can run out in front of traffic without warning, stop abruptly with trolleys and even bump into things or slip off of kerbs; some might slip on banana skins discarded by others and some might slip on icy patches or trip on uneven surfaces. Cyclists often dart in and out of traffic and are not afraid to mount pavements in order to by-pass traffic signals etc. Skate boarders also think that they are in full control of things. Sometimes, road works are underway and things like scaffolds and ladders will be present on pavements. In addition, everyone has numerous pre-occupations and distractions to contend with as well as their own individual agendas.

Obviously, if the High Street were a workplace (which it will be for a great many of course), certain hazards and risks might need to be addressed specifically and/or differently perhaps; despite which, the above is a description of a 'normal functioning' High Street. By way of a further example, let's imagine a legally compliant construction site in the UK, USA or Australia for example. Outside of such a site we might well see a safety sign stating something like the following;

- No Hard hat;

- No Goggles;

- No Protective Footwear;

- No Gloves;

- No High Visibility Vest;

- NO ENTRY!

- Site opening times: Monday to Friday 07:30-17:30.

If a construction site, or any other place of work for that matter, was a totally risk free environment then such a sign would be pointless. But, it is not pointless, it makes a clear and legally compliant statement to the contrary; risks *are* present. Perhaps, it should read differently;

- Risk of serious and fatal head injuries;

- Risk of eye injuries and blinding;

- Risk of puncture, crush and other potentially crippling injuries to feet;

- Risk of cuts, crushing and other injuries to hands;

- Risk of serious and fatal injuries from moving vehicles;

- The list is not exhaustive;

- ENTER?

- <u>Trespassers aside, sign only applies Monday to Friday 07:30-17:30.</u>

Of itself, the construction site is no more dangerous than a lamp post is (as it happens, there are no personal injury accidents on that site when there are no people present). Consequently, the inability to control certain risks any further renders them conditional insofar as they represent the "normal standing condition" of an environment in which we otherwise manage quite well. Regardless of how "unwelcome" the persisting factors might be, they are accepted and assumed to be the norm and it is this assumption, not just the inability to control, that classifies them as mere conditions (Hart & Honore 2002:36-7). For purposes here then, and only for purposes here, many of the risks remaining must be viewed as 'conditions' rather than causes since they exist regardless of whether or not an accident happens; and...they are entitled to exist.

Reason's (2004) Latent Condition

The *condition* is something that both investigators and analysts must have a firm grasp of; indeed, once the term itself is understood, it should be fairly obvious that it would be ridiculous to actually refer to it by name in either an investigation or a report. For instance, in the High Street accident, the man collided with a lamp-post, not a condition (mere or otherwise). In addition, we know that the underlying cause was a behavioural one. Consequently, we understand enough about terminology to be able to describe things coherently so that uninvolved parties have a clear picture of what happened and of what our terms mean. That said, the events and circumstances of the lamp-post accident (as with all others) can be described without reference to causal terms at all; i.e. a man walked into a lamp-post whilst the focus of his attention was elsewhere (reference to conditions or causes is unnecessary). Unfortunately, Reason's (2004) so-called "latent condition", a notion that is central to his Swiss cheese model (SCM), is not so straight-forward (at least, not immediately); indeed, there are a number of problems with it but, for now, we shall explore it via the following.

According to Reason (2004:12) the 'O' ring that failed on Space Shuttle Challenger's right side rocket booster was a "latent condition". According to Hollnagel (2004:56), a latent condition is not something that can trigger an accident as such and this is confirmed *in part* by Reason et al (2006:7) (i.e. Reason, Hollnagel and Paries) who agree that a condition is not a cause (of note for later, they stop short of saying that a *latent condition* cannot be a cause). Initially, therefore, one could be forgiven for assuming that a latent condition and a mere condition are very similar things. Indeed, Reason (2004:234) says that his latent conditions are "not quite" of the same character as Hart & Honore's mere conditions which, of course, is not the same as saying that they are wholly dissimilar concepts. However, a problem arises when we turn to the official investigation into the Challenger disaster. According to that, the failed 'O' ring on Challenger was, in fact, the *'immediate cause'* of the disaster (Committee on Science and Technology 1986) (CSaT 1986). Consequently, for purposes here, we find that the term latent condition *does* capture an expression of cause and so Reason's reference to Hart & Honore's mere conditions is, at this stage, a little odd perhaps.

A cursory look at the word latent also reveals problems. For instance, we know for a fact that the probability of an unsurvivable, temperature related 'O' ring failure on the fateful morning that Challenger launched was in no way unknown, hidden or concealed. Engineers had expressed grave concerns just the night before (Rogers Commission 1986: CSaT 1986) in relation to the anticipated temperature at launch and its likely effect on the 'O' rings. As it happened, the temperature that morning was indeed 15° colder than it had been for any other flight. As such, there was nothing latent, dormant or conditional about either the 'O' ring or the critical circumstances of the fateful launch. Consequently, it is difficult to see how Reason can consider the 'O' ring to be a condition of any description and that difficultly is not assisted by his use of the word latent. The 'O' ring failure was the immediate cause of the disaster and was neither mere, latent nor hidden. That said, we know that Reason is a founder member of the organisational accident school and a firm believer that all accidents are caused by upstream management failures. Since he has no other terms to describe a root or underlying cause then perhaps the term latent condition is a synonym for those as well. So, let's take a quick look at the underlying or proximate cause of the Challenger disaster (bearing in mind that we do so *only* to explore the latent condition).

According to CSaT (1986:4-5), the "underlying" or "fundamental problem" causing the disaster was "poor technical decision-making over a period of several years by top NASA and contractor personnel... ." For purposes here, that statement shows responsibility being shifted far away in both space and time from what some might have initially thought the actual underlying (root or proximate) cause to have been; i.e. the decision to launch that was made in the immediate time frame of the disaster by those in possession of the relevant information. Nevertheless, such a move away from the sharp-end and into the abyss of the so-called blunt-end is fully in keeping with Reason's (2004) notion of the organisational accident (discussed later below). Indeed, Reason (1990/2003:192) concurs that the underlying or root cause of the 'O' ring failure could be traced back over a nine year period. Of course, it should be noted that Reason has merely applied the SCM retrospectively once again and agreed with what some might feel was an erroneous and counter-productive conclusion by CSat.

Consequently, and whilst we shall look at the term in more detail later, we find that the latent condition is in *no way* similar to a *mere condition* (which, places a massive question mark over why Reason made any reference to Hart & Honore whatsoever). Applied retrospectively, as it has been once again here by Reason, the latent condition reveals itself to be a notion that merges both immediate and root cause. However, since a condition cannot be a cause, the word condition in its title becomes unnecessarily misleading. A latent condition, clearly, is a combined expression of cause that defaults to become a singular expression of what would otherwise be called a 'root cause'. That said, we must also bear in mind for now that the mere condition remains to be *associated* with it in some way.

Before moving on, it has been found that the further you move away from the point in space and time of the critical act or event, the less effective any remedial intervention strategy becomes (TYS). Yet, in the after-math of the Columbia disaster some 17 years after Challenger, NASA opted to move still further away from the 'sharp-end' having been sold on the idea that organisations cause accidents (CAIB 2003).

PART 1 INTERIM SUMMARY

According to Petersen, management "invariably" cause all accidents. A man cannot be the root or proximate cause (i.e. the sole cause) of any accident and he is never responsible for his own actions since his actions are caused, "invariably", by someone, or something, else. Every *thing, act, omission, cause* or *condition* that might in some way be involved or associated with an accident is entitled to be called a symptom of upstream managerial failings.

That, is an absurdity.

For purposes here, that absurdity results from the naivety and inexperience of certain academics and writers who, like many untrained analysts or investigators (and many that are, apparently, 'trained'), are unable (if not unprepared or reluctant) to distinguish between what are causes and what are not.

When Petersen rejected the common cause hypothesis he compelled himself to ignore man and look to the wider environment for causal alternatives. However, numerous root causes do not exist and they are not, and cannot be, selected at random. Root cause reveals itself when, and only when, the objectivity and skill of the investigator is such that he is able to ignore or discount the numerous antecedents and conditions that always exist.

Once found or suspected, the application of commonsense, logic and knowledge of the basic distinctions between causes and conditions either confirms or rejects the factor being put forward as *the cause*. When such are applied to the so-called 'root causes' 'identified' by multiple causation theory, they are rejected; indeed, they ought never to have been identified as such in the first place since they are irrelevant to the central causal enquiry.

Of course, many of the conditions under the spotlight throughout this book should, ideally, *not exist*. Often, they represent regulatory breaches, system non-conformances or improvement opportunities.

However, the way in which such things are dealt with tend to be specified as arrangements that detail matters like audit and inspection regimes and reporting processes. These matters, important though they are, do not concern this book; this book is concerned with *causation.*

By the very nature of its premise, multiple causation theory does not require any of its so-called root causes to be tested or confirmed since its causative assumption is categoric and unrelenting. However, had any form of accepted test been installed into, or properly considered by, *any* such theory, that test alone would have disproved it. Thus, both empirical data and logic disprove multiple causation theory.

In reality, multiple causation theory equates, ridiculously, to strict liability. But, even the law recognises, where strict liability genuinely needs to apply as a matter of public policy, that a convicted defendant will not, and cannot, always be guilty in the causative sense. Furthermore, multiple causation theory is obviously attractive to regulators where, under the general criminal law as it applies to health and safety offences for instance, causation does not need to be proved. Consequently, they are essentially free to allude to all types of failure without having to make any causative link. However, the ability to attach strict liability or to convict without proof of cause is not a luxury that extends to writers, academics or safety practitioners.

Chapter Two Part 2:
Death by Analysis

Cause and Causal Attribution

Unfortunately, when an accident does happen, the many parties to its investigation will each form a subjective view of cause (Mackie 1993) that is aligned to their individual interest (Dekker 2002: Woods & Cook 2002). Often, these views are forged against a backdrop of blame and responsibility that references what each party can, or thinks they can, control (Collingwood 1940). Indeed, the way that some individuals (Jones & Nisbett 1972) and groups (Pettigrew 1979) make causal attributions is better described as engrained and predictable.

When behaviour is under the spotlight, those engrained tendencies will be juxtaposed and at odds with each other. As a result, some will be inclined to offer dispositional attributions for the behaviour insofar as their tendency is to focus on individual 'faults' at the expense of any situational or environmental influences. On the other hand, at the opposite extreme, others will be offering situational attributions for the behaviour insofar as they are inclined *not* to focus on certain individuals (i.e. those at the so-called sharp end). For instance, the individual that walked into the High Street lamp-post would be seen as a bit of a 'numpty' from the dispositional point of view; he should look where he is going and concentrate more. However, the situational view might argue that the lamp-post shouldn't be there; council planners didn't think about it very well; or, the window that he was busy admiring himself in out of the corner of his eye should have been blacked out to reduce the temptation for people to use it as a mirror.

Consequently, unanimous opinion (recall HSE 2003c above), let alone any common ground, is impossible and prevention suffers.

Such juxtaposed views on cause cannot, of course, be based on any agreed form of objective reasoning or criteria; if they were, unanimous opinion would result far more often than it does. As it is, risk management systems, safety management policies, practices and procedures etc are based on laws and codes that are open to extremes of interpretation. If these extremes are prone more to the subjective whim of causal attribution than they are to factual causal analysis, then industry should take stock; not least of its investigative practices and the philosophies on which they are based. Furthermore, if causal attribution is indeed this powerful then the philosophy, interpretation and practical application of safety will be similarly affected. If so, the validity of post-accident decisions regarding remedial intervention or system improvements will be highly questionable.

En route to the new millennium theory, it soon became apparent that a vast array of notions, diagrams, models and 'so-called theories' were circulating the relevant communities. However, everything appeared to be the result of the latest academic work or fad. As such, the 'age' of those spoken to during the TYS tended to determine the model that they would identify as their preference. That is, depending on when they had studied and where, the model adopted and retained could be linked to the most influentially relevant period of their training and development. Before they would adopt or consider an alternative model, its philosophy would have to be similar in their eyes to the one that they preferred or tended to use; unless, of course, it could be logically shown to be flawed or the product of a by-gone era (even then, removing the infection of the previous model, theory or philosophy is extremely difficult).

In essence then, the general background of the investigator or analyst instils a bias (Lewycky 1987: Lekberg 1997) that may not be the result of any factual and objective causal reasoning. Indeed, such biases tend to result from infection akin to 'group think' (Janis 1982) amongst the relevant communities and their latest protégés; consequently, hindsight and confirmation bias are denied as having played any part in either their views or findings. Therefore, we should remain alert to the fact that it is the questions that we ask which determine the answers that we get; and, of course, those that we do not get (Zohar 1997:60).

Death on a Sunday

The text herein is for industrial accident investigators working at the sharp end; investigators who are aware that hundreds of thousands of workers have died in the USA simply doing the job they do...this, since the introduction of the 1970 Occupational, Safety and Health Act. Similarly, this side of the water, we know that tens of thousands of UK workers have also died simply doing the job they do...this, since the introduction of the Health and Safety at Work etc Act 1974.

Let's then move away from lamp-posts for a moment and reflect on the reality of death at the sharp end; a reality that academic spectators (most of whom do not have accident investigator in their job descriptions) usually read and write about rather than endure.

Whenever the following tragedy unfolds in my mind, I am compelled to think also of the death of another much loved and respected man; a Foreman, killed during a lifting operation he was supervising.

On a cold damp Rembrance Sunday morning, whilst I was dealing with the after-math of that Foreman's death, a man unbeknown to me at the time had died on an unrelated site just two miles away. A heavy steel structure he was working on had become unstable due solely to his own actions upon it. Its movement was such that it came to rest up against another structure leaving him trapped between them. He was left in an upright position, as if just stood there, but with his feet dangling some 6 inches off of the ground. Five years later, I would be engaged by the defence team.

The statements that I had to read, the photographs that I had to look at and the people to whom I spoke conveyed nought but a scene of pure horror. The weight was such that it compressed his chest and torso massively. No more air would he breathe and no more use were his vital organs. The trauma caused him to urinate and defecate beneath the many layers of clothing that had kept him warm that morning. His eyeballs were bulging from their sockets and his tongue had been forced far out of his mouth. His poor face, frozen in time with an expression of shock and terror, was the colour of blue which tells you that life has since departed. His hands, as if grasping on to the last vestiges of life, had clenched tightly. In one hand, the burning torch that he had been using was still lit...and still held firm. But, his arms, by the instant so hopelessly lifeless, dropped immediately and limply to his side. His torch, obeying none but the laws of nature, then quickly proceeded to set him on fire.

But maybe not, maybe I shouldn't tell you about this. Perhaps you do not need to imagine the stench of faeces or of burnt flesh. Perhaps you do not need to hear of the bewilderment that the scene conveyed to his friends and colleagues. 'Why', they asked, his body partially concealed by one of the structures, 'is he not trying to put the flames out'. Sadly, it would not be until after they had extinguished him that the full horror would begin to become obvious; upon the stark realisation of which, one turned to the others and simply said...'he's gone'...'he's dead'. Perhaps the visions that will haunt his family, friends and colleagues for the rest of their lives should remain theirs and theirs alone. Perhaps we should just say a prayer in the hope that it might assist them when next, in those dark and haunting moments of sleep, their subconscious reawakens the demons that will forever force them to relive those horrific events. No, I think we will leave this here for a moment (returning to it shortly below) and turn to an alternative. However, before we do, I have inferred that memories tend only to haunt us in the darker hours; that, is not true.

A Haunting Encounter

Some years past, as part of my investigation into the events and circumstances surrounding a young man's death, I had occasion to attend his home and speak to his mother. They had lived alone together for the past 10 years since the sudden death of the boy's father. During a number of searching and extremely difficult (for us both) questions, I asked her what sort of time her son would normally get home from work.

She said, "I always come into the kitchen and put the kettle on at 4:45 p.m. ...I always have a cup of tea waiting for him when he gets here at 4:55 p.m." I then asked her about the events of the fateful day and she said "I came into the kitchen and he was stood by the sink". Somewhat puzzled, I asked her what time this would have been and she said that it was "exactly 4:45 p.m.". She looked at me quite blankly and so I felt compelled to ask her if anything was said between them. "Oh yes", she replied, "he said, don't worry mum, everything is OK". She then added "I went back into the sitting room and about 5 minutes later I got the knock on the door...you know", holding back her tears, "the police".

What she said took me completely by surprise and has stayed with me to this day. Whatever encounter she was referring to in her kitchen, it was not one that she could possibly have had with her son...he had been declared dead at the scene at 16:02.

When Death Calls the Shots – A Case Study

'J' tripped over a 75mm diameter hose that was running across the path to the site canteen. He suffered a fall to the same level, a light sprain to his wrist, grazes to his face and was off work for two days. On his second day back to work he began to feel unwell and was sent home. The exact medical cause is of no importance here but, sadly, he died later that evening.

The death prompted an all too common, narrow focussed, knee-jerk investigation that resulted in the following findings;

- Work in a near-by trench had been poorly planned.

- Whilst the trench was only 15 inches deep, the requirement for Permits to Work should be extended to cover all excavations, regardless of depth.

- The Supervisor of the men in the trench was uncooperative. He claimed that site management had instructed him not to dig up the path and, in any event, he said that to dig it up was not reasonably practicable and that he had not priced to do that anyway. He said that in view of the information given to him, the time of year and the nature of the ground, the water that entered the trench could not have been foreseen by him. As regards the hose that he had placed across the path he said that people should watch where they are going; we put two signs out. Adding, I've had my eight men with me for five years and we have'nt had one reportable accident; this is a construction site not a play-ground; this is a witch hunt.

- The risk assessment for the work in the trench had not specified the potential for people to trip over hoses; if it had, the hose would have been buried for the duration of the job and the accident would have been prevented.

- The signs warning of the hose were clearly inadequate.

- The Supervisor has not received any recognised safety training. This should be considered for inclusion into the mandatory requirements for approving contractors. The process of selecting contractors should receive a general review.

- Local management are not controlling contractors effectively.

- There were various items of litter along the pathway; housekeeping is poor.

- Managers and supervisors are to be reminded of their responsibilities.

- 'J' was finishing a mobile call that he took in the canteen. He said that canteen staff had told him to leave as they had to clean up. He was ending his call at the time of the accident and simply didn't see the hose; he knows that phones should only be used in offices or canteens. Opening times of the canteen should be extended to enable people to leave in an orderly fashion rather than being herded out.

- Apart from numerous breaches of the law and other contributory factors, this accident was caused by poorly planned and inadequately supervised work in a trench adjacent to the canteen pathway.

If the investigator had been asked to conduct a workplace inspection then the above findings might be relevant; however, in the instant case, they are not. The findings present clear improvement opportunities but none of them will address *the* cause of the accident since *the* cause has not been identified; it awaits detection and, hence, the next victim.

A Simple Analysis of the Accident

The 75mm hose had been across the pathway for three days. Discounting other users of the path and any unreported falls or near-misses, 60 men, including 'J', had stepped over, or on, the hose six times each day. Therefore, over the three days, there were 1079 successful negotiations of the hose prior to 'J's accident.

Clearly, that particular accident would not have occurred if the hose had not been there (in much the same way that the lamp-post accident would not have occurred had the lamp-post not been there). But, the hose was also a feature on 1079 occasions when *no* accident occurred. Consequently, for purely preventative purposes, the hose becomes a 'condition' in the events and circumstance rather than the cause.

Notwithstanding that the hose, ideally, should not have been there perhaps, it misleads investigators, those who act upon reports and prevention in general if such conditions are seen as causes. Worse still is the effect of terminology which suggests that mere conditions might in some way be latent, concealed or unknown. Rather than view the hose as latent, prevention requires that we acknowledge it as something that was, in fact, blatant. That said, we must remain conscious of the fact that it was blatantly obvious to those men on the scene, not to the organisation or the system.

Deeper Analysis

Although 'J' was using a mobile phone at the time of his accident, the investigator did not identify that as being something that could have *made the difference*. If it had, then the question for analytical purposes would have been, in the absence of the phone (not the hose), does this accident occur. Even then, it is not the phone itself that is the cause of this 'type' of accident; rather, it is the distraction of the conversation (Loeb & Clarke 2009). Often, the distraction or preoccupation causes an error which is itself then "primarily responsible" for the accident (Firenze 1973).

As a 'condition', the hose has not caused the accident. To say that a hose or a lamp-post could be some sort of 'psychological precursor' (Reason 1990) to the accident or a provoker of error or violation (Reason 2004) requires a serious re-think. The mere condition, and any similar notion within a latent condition, has no such capacity since it is an inert factor upon which the error or violation must act to produce an accident. Therefore, and whilst the hose appears causally related to the untrained or biased eye, its relationship to 'J's accident is coincidental i.e. it is something that is associated with the accident, not causative of it. Consequently, care is required to ensure that it is not just the 'coincidental' or circumstantial that is attended to since that will leave *the* cause unaddressed.

The investigator has defaulted to blame the system (hence management or the organisation) under the belief that the system already has controls or barriers in place that should counter this type of accident. In the vast majority of cases considered by the TYS, that was found to be a mistaken belief; as was the belief that the 'very fact' of an accident usually means that "one or more barriers have failed" (Hollnagel 2004:68). The most that an investigator can assume from the mere fact of an accident is that a risk was present (*Chargot*). Furthermore, as we shall see immediately below and later, accidents (such as those forming part of the many statistics touched upon earlier above) can and regularly do occur, *despite* the existence of a fully compliant system.

Returning to the Sunday morning tragedy introduced at p.59 above, the Crown Prosecutor was unsuccessful first time round. Undeterred, and presumably in the 'public interest', he went to the Court of Appeal where it was decided that the case should go back to the Crown Court; following which, six and a half years after the death, the Judge delivered a ruling of no case to answer. Amongst the points he made, fully acknowledging the respect that everyone had for the deceased, were these;

There can be a disjuncture between risk that is created by the process as a whole and the risk assumed by an individual. If such risk cannot be foreseen then it cannot be said that the defendants exposed him to it. There was not a shred of evidence either to criticise the defendants nor show want on their part. To conclude otherwise would be tantamount to saying that the very fact of the accident proves dereliction of duty. Even where the duty is qualified so far as is practicable, to expect the defendant to be able to manage the unforeseeable would be illogical. Constant supervision was not required and what the deceased did, for reasons that nobody will now ever know, was wholly at odds with his instructions. With the greatest of respect for those touched by this man's death, nobody can resile from having to make a realistic and commonsense assessment of what he did that day (R v Norwest).

What the system needs is information about what it is that is defeating it (not a denial that such is possible); only then can it improve. However, and depending on the interest of those involved, that opportunity for improvement tends to be viewed as a weakness in the system that was obvious before hand via the academic and regulatory crystal ball; hindsight bias reigning supreme (Sherwood-Jones 2009). Indeed, the safety community in general is aligned to the academic and regulatory position.

The effect in many organisations has been to move away from the critical matter of error and behaviour. Such moves away have been further encouraged by those such as Cook *et al* (1998) who believe that there is always a cause beyond the unsafe or deliberate act; and, that such causes are always organisationally or systemically driven.

More damaging still are the appalling appeals to emotion from writers such as Reason (2000) who feel that we gain some sort of emotional satisfaction from "blaming individuals" (strong words from the author of a model that, as we shall see, persistently blames individuals other than those directly involved). Of course, Reason's view is as ridiculous and unfounded as it is offensive. Those who genuinely support such views are part and parcel of a problem (discussed shortly) that Heinrich (1941) thought would be gone by the end of the 1990s. As it is, investigations that are driven by a denial of human error and behaviour (of 'unsafe acts' or 'human failures'), whilst purporting to be deep and complex, are actually taking the easy way out; management presents a soft, grey target. Cursed by the rigours of confirmation bias and erroneous reasoning (by the digby effect perhaps), they run their respective employers and clients around and round in circles; perpetually fire fighting, perpetually chasing their own tails. So that the problem is not understated, Reason (2004:236) concedes that the number of latent conditions identified by investigations like 'J's when using the 'Swiss cheese model' are not dependent on the "sickness of the system" but, on the length of time that one is prepared to keep unearthing them!

Before moving on then, note once again that the above discussions on the 'mere condition' are intended to assist both analysis and remedial intervention. They are not some sort of concealment of blame nor are they some veiled attempt to say that men should simply be more careful around hazards that should not be there; already stated, those who think that way are, in fact, part of the problem, not the solution.

Part 2 INTERIM SUMMARY

Writers such as Hollnagel, Reason and Petersen are compelled to align themselves to the situational school since sharp-end man can *never* be *the cause* according to them. However, cursed by the digby effect, confirmation and hindsight bias, they are compelled not only to deny free will but, the very nature of human behaviour itself.

Tragically, highly competent men do kill and injure themselves as a result of nothing more than their own freely chosen, and legally unfettered, actions. Far more often, clearly, than the academic realises, there is a disjuncture between risk that is created by the organisation and that which is created and assumed by the individual.

Chapter Three:
Heinrich's Accident Causation Theory

Heinrich's Accident Sequence

Heinrich's *accident sequence* was introduced in the early 1930s (Heinrich 1941:13). Following an analysis of 75,000 plant and closed claim insurance records (Heinrich et al 1980), Heinrich identified five factors that he felt were common in injury producing and property damage accidents (Fig.hdom).

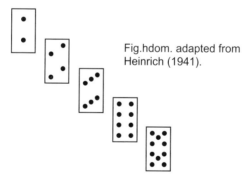

Fig.hdom. adapted from Heinrich (1941).

In addition, Heinrich found that the events and circumstances in both injury and damage producing accidents invariably followed a fixed and logical order. As each factor appeared dependent on another, he likened them to a row of dominoes in that one stood or fell depending on whether the preceding one stood or fell. (Fig. h1). Of interest for later, supporters of multiple causation and Reason's SCM for instance argue that most accident sequences are not so straight-forward. However, at an end-note in his book on the so-called organisational accident, Reason (2004:1) references Shell Expro's finding that their fatal accidents typically result from a single chain of events. That said, and as we shall see below, the vast majority of accident sequences are, in fact, far more straight-forward even than Heinrich's the depiction.

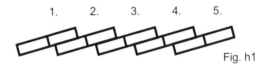

Fig. h1

Heinrich's Dominoes

For purposes here, Heinrich's description of each of his dominoes can be summarised as follows;

Domino 1. Ancestry and Social Environment.
This domino represents traits of character (what Heinrich refers to at domino 2. as 'Faults of Person') such as recklessness (a tendency towards at risk behaviour in certain circumstances perhaps) inconsiderateness and nervousness (aversion to risk or tending to hesitancy perhaps). Heinrich (1941:13:109) considers that both inheritance and the social environment "cause faults of person".

Domino 2. Fault(s) of Person.
At domino 2., Heinrich (1944:14) says that "inherited or acquired faults of person...constitute the proximate reasons for committing unsafe acts or for the existence of mechanical or physical hazards" (i.e. conditions). Consequently, domino 2. effectively becomes the *proximate cause* of *all* accidents.

That said, it is important for this book's purposes that we move forward from here aware that *reasons* or explanations for unsafe acts do not alter their status as proximate causes (Difford 2004); indeed,

70

Difford says (and we will ultimately agree) that domino 2. should not really be considered to be part of Heinrich's causation theory at all.

Domino 3. Unsafe act and/or Condition.
Domino number three (Fig. h2), representing the *immediate cause* of the accidents analysed by Heinrich, is labelled as "unsafe performance of persons" and "mechanical or physical hazards" (Heinrich 1941:14). His theory states, quite correctly, that if there is no unsafe act and/or condition, then a preventable accident cannot occur.

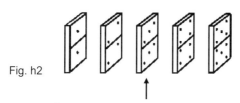

Fig. h2

Remove domino number **3,** the unsafe act
and/or condition, and a preventable accident
cannot happen.

Acts of God aside, Heinrich (1941:20) found that 88% of the accidents in his study were caused by unsafe acts and 10% by unsafe conditions. However, the TYS was unable to support that distinction insofar as it is not possible to identify the proximate cause of an unsafe condition beyond the fact that an unsafe act (suitably defined) must either have created it or allowed others to be exposed to it; whilst Heinrich (1941:14) was aware of this, it needed clarifying owing to its potential to confuse. Indeed, Haddon *et al* (1964:252) have described the practice of assigning cause to one or the other as "misleading" since both inevitably result from human behaviour.

Domino 4. Accident.
Heinrich (1941:15) describes an accident as an event with the potential to cause injury.

Domino 5. Injury.
Here, he lists things like fractures and lacerations that result from certain accidents.

Dominoes 1-3 Revisited

If we consider Heinrich's accident sequence from a commonsense or practical perspective, it should be obvious that his *theory* on causation itself relates only to dominoes 2. & 3. (notwithstanding the earlier contention that domino 2. represents a reason or explanation, not a cause). In reality, domino 1. can only be a statement of his personal beliefs since it is inconceivable that he made any such causative finding during his analysis; that is, he cannot possibly have found that all accidents were traceable (through the unsafe or deliberate act) to acquired or inherited faults. Indeed, as we shall see, Bird (1974) and Reason (2004) have also rejected that claim even though their rejections are necessary in order to support alternative causative beliefs. In any event, Heinrich (1941:18) says that it should only be necessary to look to the factor that immediately preceded the unsafe act etc unless there is an obvious need to "dig into the background" to "accomplish results". Of course, in the context there, results relate to remedial options and it should be noted therefore that Heinrich's (1941:17) factors in the accident sequence constituted "an index of the kind of information that the preventionist must deal with."

Consequently, Heinrich's views on the causes of a person's faults as expressed by dominoes 1. & 2. (i.e. the causes of causes of causes) should be handled with caution. Indeed, and whilst supportive of the essence of the theory, Difford (1998) offers that the exceptionless causal statement inferred by dominoes 1., 2. & 3. is impossible; not least, it ignores a simple error in a fully compliant workplace committed by a man whose 'make-up' is such that he would never knowingly break the rules. That, and other reasons and examples aside, he therefore argues that domino 1. is a fiction in the causative sense since *proximate cause* is identified at domino 2. As such, he argues that the only causative statement that Heinrich should have made is essentially as per the depiction in Fig.ah1. below. That said,

Difford notes that most investigators will describe both the accident and the immediate cause in one statement; e.g. "following a slip on some oil that he hadn't noticed on the kitchen floor, Jim fell and injured his elbow". In practice, he therefore offers that the immediate cause and the accident are catered for in a single statement (i.e. in a single domino) and that, as a result, the only other 'domino' that logically needs identifying is the one relating to proximate cause (Fig.ah2.); that, 'acts of God' (suitably defined) aside, can only be human behaviour suitably defined (Difford 2004).

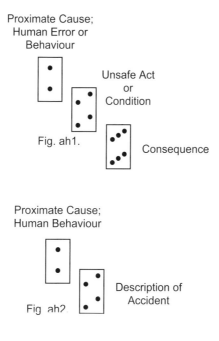

Proximate Cause;
Human Error or
Behaviour

Unsafe Act
or
Condition

Fig. ah1.

Consequence

Proximate Cause;
Human Behaviour

Description of
Accident

Fig ah2.

Of similar importance here, Difford offers that the wider effect has been to inadvertently convince certain academics and writers (e.g. Bird 1974: Reason 2004) that a causative link will *always* exist between dominoes (or Swiss cheese slices) 1. and 5.; i.e. that the proximate cause will *never* be domino 2. but, invariably and unconditionally, domino 1. Of course, as we shall see, Bird and

Reason moved a million miles away from Heinrich's findings in order to claim (based on their own subjective re-labelling of things) that the cause of a man's behaviour, without exception, is due to management or organisational failures. However, Williams (2011) offers that such exceptionless statements of cause are absurd; a view (discussed later below) that is similarly shared by many (e.g. Hart & Honore 2002; O'Connor 1995; Botham 2008; Lowe 2002). Ignoring domino 1. completely, Williams reminds IIAI Certified Lead Investigators of Heinrich's (1941:104) definition of proximate cause; that is...

The "unsafe personal act or unsafe mechanical hazard that results directly in an accident."

Williams also reminds us that Heinrich was employed in the insurance sector and that he would have been logically guided by definitions from cases such as *Pawsey* v *Scottish Union & National Insurance [1907]* (Ivamy 1993:415) and the American case of *Lynn Gas* v *Meriden Fire Insurance (Mass 1893)*; according to the latter, proximate cause is...

"the active and efficient cause that sets in motion a train of events which brings about a result without the intervention of any force started and working actively from a new and independent source".

Relying in part on Kalis *et al* (1997: 2004; 13-21) then, proximate cause is *the cause* that sets in motion the chain of events that, unbroken by any intervening or independent causes, produces the loss and without which the loss would not have occurred. Such a 'norm' or operational definition is vitally important. It allows us to cut short the chain of causal antecedents that would otherwise see 'analysis' go on (as it does with the SCM for instance) for ever. As Williams (2010) puts it, if we take Heinrich at face value then the cause of any accident is apparently traceable through the relevant individual's deliberate act and back in time to their great, great, great grandfather (or beyond).

Causes of an Underlying Nature

Whilst Heinrich (1941:104) uses an array of causal terms throughout his book, he warns that the term cause "cannot be used loosely". However, in addition to terms like basic cause, subcause, indirect cause, direct and proximate cause, he also refers to what he calls causes of an "underlying nature". Unfortunately, that term is potentially problematic since it has a meaning today that it did not have when Heinrich used it in the 1930s. Back then, he said that "the term underlying cause refers to managerial and supervisory faults and to social and environmental conditions that are outside of the work place". Consequently, and by way of clarification, we must note that Heinrich (1941: 109-10) makes it clear that these "indirect causes" are of "less significance than the proximate causes".

There is no doubt that Heinrich's was the most significant work as regards focussing management on its responsibility to provide safe places and systems of work etc. But, he felt that it was "unwise" to "depend automatically" on engineering controls, supervision and training when the "accident problem centers about unsafe personal practice". He said that "by far the most sensible" thing to do is to try and understand the reasons why men act unsafely (Heinrich 1941:35; Heinrich & Lateiner 1969). However, Heinrich (1941:8 & 243) offered that *"the complete ideal program of accident prevention awaits the millennium"* since industry was *"not yet receptive enough to take the next logical step – which is that of accident psychology"*.

Such statements, clearly, identify the need to incorporate behavioural strategies into the management of health and safety; i.e. to view behavioural safety as an inseparable and constitutional part of the entire program such that no one aspect of the program has any right to take precedence over another. Consequently, the reader should note that Heinrich's use of the term underlying cause was not an invitation to make management causatively responsible for all unsafe acts. On the contrary, he was fully aware, as were many others (e.g. Suchman 1970:4; Robens-Cmnd 5034:9; HSE 2002:1) that physical hazards were becoming less important as a factor in accidents. Already noted, and years ahead of his time, Heinrich (1941:16) advised industry that it would eventually *have to* expand its safety related work into the "underlying field of human behaviour". Until such time as it does (bearing in mind Difford's and the TYS numerous findings and warnings on the subject), a massively profitable field (in more ways than one) lies untapped.

Heinrich's Theory and Sequence in General

Heinrich's simplistic description has lead many to assume that his depiction of the accident sequence can be taken literally. That is, that five immediately obvious and sequentially explicit factors will present themselves to the investigator of an injury producing accident. However, the TYS did not find (nor did it expect to find) that to be the case in practice and the sequence shown by Heinrich should, in fact, never occur in reality. To assume otherwise would mean that an investigator, within his report, would be making causative references to things like heredity, environmental influences beyond the workplace and 'undesirable' traits.

The events and circumstances leading to an injury (and, hence, any perception of temporal orderliness) can only emerge (if such exists) following a well informed reconstruction according to the evidence gathered. Those events and circumstances, provided that they do not break the causal chain in the practical sense, can be removed in both space and time (noting that the relevant unsafe or deliberate act remains to be the focus). The task for the investigator is to produce a rendering of those events and circumstances that is as concise as possible; this, so that the reader is informed as opposed to being overwhelmed and stupefied. Furthermore, it would assist researchers to bear in mind that Heinrich's work was predominantly concerned with accident prevention, not accident causation or investigation. It would also assist them to recognise that the unsafe act, the unsafe condition and the loss often occur simultaneously; and, more often than not, spontaneously.

Heinrich's (1944) Three Domino Sequence

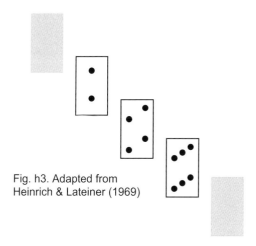

Fig. h3. Adapted from
Heinrich & Lateiner (1969)

During the training of managers and supervisors, Heinrich (1944) would ignore dominoes 1. and 5. (Fig. H3) and describe the remaining three as follows;

Domino 1. Fault of person.

Domino 2. Unsafe or improper practice or condition.

Domino 3. Injury or production loss.

The essential premise of the theory remains in that it is the removal of the central domino (number 2 here) that is necessary to prevent the accident. Difford (1998) sees the loss of domino number five as better highlighting the fact that, where accidents of the same type are involved, there is no difference between an accident sequence that results in loss and one that narrowly avoids it (i.e. a near-miss).

The Accident-Error Domino Sequence

In Heinrich & Lateiner's work entitled 'Management and Controlling Employee Behaviour', it is worth noting here that the three domino sequence is shown under a heading of 'The Accident-Error Domino Sequence'. In addition, regarding the absence of the original domino number one, it was offered that "there is nothing immediately effective that a foreman can do about the ancestry of a faulty person" (Heinrich & Lateiner 1969:222).

Suchman's (1961) Operational Definition

For Suchman (1961:246), the accident can be thought of as "progressing through a series of stages". He offers that whilst the initial focus will be on the immediate events, the accident began at some earlier stage and *just where to cut the developmental sequence* [how to employ or devise a stop rule perhaps] *is a problem of operational definition*". He therefore recommends viewing the accident sequence as three broad segments (See fig.S1).

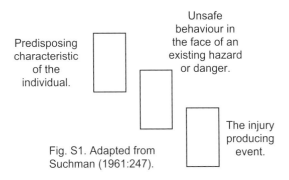

Predisposing characteristic of the individual.

Unsafe behaviour in the face of an existing hazard or danger.

The injury producing event.

Fig. S1. Adapted from Suchman (1961:247).

A Note On The So-called Stop Rule

In Fansler's (1959) earlier mentioned study he offered that the road traffic accident sequence essentially commences when the driver "climbs into the car and drives off". Of course, depending on the nature and length of the journey, the focus of attention may well be on a point in time much closer to the accident itself. Alternatively, it might extend further back in time if, for instance, a component failure is traced to an earlier inspection failure on a mechanic's part or even an original manufacturing problem. Either way, recalling Heinrich's (1941:1959), Lateiner & Heinrich's (1969) and Suchman's (1960) "operational definition", we will always be looking at human behaviour (Haddon et al 1964). Regardless of whether it is an error on a driver or mechanic's part or a failure at original manufacture, the system must be informed of the exact area of personal responsibility that failed if it is to improve. As such, our operational definition demands that we consider "acts" (Suchman 1961). Furthermore, we must also have an accepted test for potential improvement opportunities and root causes (ISO 9001).

In such cases, where the view of cause is operationally and factually defined, the resulting investigation will be balanced, pragmatic and objective. Working backwards in time from the event being enquired into (i.e. the effect), the investigator moves from transitive cause to transitive cause. According to the only logical and defensible operational definition that exists, the investigator will halt at the relevant unsafe or deliberate act. That deliberate act represents the barrier between the transitive causes and those that represent the upstream antecedent causal chain; i.e. that barrier would be the stop rule for academic purposes. At that point, in-depth remedial analysis takes place. Unless the analysis indicates that further evidence gathering is required (noting importantly that this is highly unlikely ever to alter the status of the deliberate act that has been found), the next phase is the consideration of remedial options followed by a selection of that which is most appropriate for the business. The option selected should then be tested and analysed for its effect on both the problem and the business before being installed. Once installed, the final phase is then the monitoring of the effectiveness of the remedy and, if it proves satisfactory, the natural close out and stopping point of the investigation is reached.

In the main, questions regarding the nature and whereabouts of the 'stop rule' (Rasmussen 1990) are born of an academic assumption that there is some sort of arbitrary rule that determines how far back an investigation should go and where or why it should eventually stop. However, that is not the case as the above description of an operationally defined investigation shows; in fact, the notion of a 'stop rule' is alien to most investigators (TYS). More often than not, questions regarding why an investigation stopped when it did are raised by those who think that it should have gone much further back in time (TYS); i.e. away from the sharp-end and into the abyss of the blunt-end (e.g. away from the obvious causes of a man's sunburn and, via cloud cuckoo land, into the realms of council policy on public access to beaches). For these, cause is presumed to be complex and random (i.e. organisationally driven and multi-faceted) and their investigations cannot therefore be guided by any logically, defensible operational definition. As such, a stop rule for them becomes unnecessary since there is no limit to how far back (or sideways) they can, or will, go; no limit at all. As a result, decisions on where to stop such investigations can only be made subjectively. That said, academics do employ a stop rule but it is one that works through the irrelevant antecedent causal chain to stop, ultimately and without exception, at management.

In many organisations, not only is there an absence of operational definition, there is usually an absence of any clear scope of work or instruction for the investigator (TYS). Consequently, and whilst there is no suggestion whatsoever here to conceal evidence, investigators tend to uncover numerous pieces of inconsequential and legally negative evidence; usually, in the form of mere conditions. Consequently, we should remind ourselves of Suchman's (1961) earlier warning that epidemiological type models tend to identify 'things' that are associated with accidents, not 'things' that are causative of them.

INTERIM SUMMARY

Acts of God (or, more correctly, the unpredictable and uncontrollable consequences of natural phenomena) aside, human behaviour, irrefutably, will be the proximate cause of any preventable accident. Indeed, writers or theorists, regardless of their views on cause, have neither valid nor logical reason to install any more dominoes or slices of cheese into their models than is depicted at Fig.ah2 below.

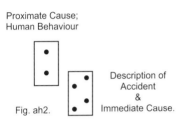

Proximate Cause;
Human Behaviour

Fig. ah2.

Description of
Accident
&
Immediate Cause.

What is more, and regardless of the labels attached to any additional upstream factors, writers such as Petersen, Bird and Reason needed to coherently express and validate their belief that, invariably and unconditionally, they could always trace *the cause* through the deliberate act that would otherwise be domino 1. above. However, and irrespective at this time of concoctions such as the latent condition which purport to be able to do that, commonsense, logic and experts in causation state, categorically, that they cannot. Even if it may sometimes be necessary to dig a little deeper beyond a deliberate act, those who claim that it can (and must) be done in order to find the cause, invariably and unconditionally on the occasion of each and every accident, render themselves ridiculous. Even if we were to find something beyond the deliberate act, that is highly unlikely ever to alter its status as the proximate cause.

Clearly, insurmountable problems are beginning to present themselves to those who profess that numerous interacting organisational factors combine, without exception, to cause all accidents. That said, support for such notions is often claimed to lie within the science of epidemiology; consequently, we will turn next to that.

Chapter Four:
Epidemiology –
Infectious Agent and Placebo!

Epidemiological Models and the Metaphoric Quest for Cause

Heinrich (1941) felt that the industrial accident problem was such that it could be compared to an epidemic. As it happens, he was one of the first industrial authors to draw attention to terms like 'agency' and the need to consider certain conditions and the susceptibility or personal factors of the individual involved. However, it should be noted that he made but a passing comparison to accidents as epidemics, and that is all. Some years later, Gordon (1949) introduced the concept of host (man), agent (the chainsaw perhaps) and environment to the epidemiological community; unfortunately, he would later offer that host, agent and environment all contribute (via interaction) to cause an accident (Hilgenkamp 2006). However, and whilst that was unsubstantiated, many have failed to appreciate that the science of epidemiology is concerned with the incidence of disease in populations. As a result, specific causation is beyond it since it is not able to address the question of what caused a particular individual's disease (Green et al 2000:381).

Nonetheless, the concept of the host, agent, environment 'triad' gradually filtered into certain factions of industry. As a result, the later notion of multiple causation theory in the general industrial setting was seen (Lingard & Rowlinson 2005) as having been given some sort of scientific basis and support from the epidemiological community.

But, and clearly aware of the developing trend, Heinrich (1959:xii:308) again drew specific attention to his earlier 'analogy with medicine'. In an attempt to clarify things he said that "in the average case, accident prevention is effectively accomplished through knowledge and application of the basic principles plus a general *knowledge of the sciences* or of specific industrial operations". Whilst accepting the obvious differences in the aetiology of disease compared to that of traumatic industrial injury, he emphasised that *"there is no variation whatever* in the principles and basic methods of prevention" (italics as per Heinrich:308). In addition, Suchman (1961:250), a distinguished pioneer of medical sociology (Tuckett & Kaufert 1978), had specifically advised against an industrial application of the epidemiological model. He suspected that the factors of host, agent and environment would show themselves to be only *"indirectly related"* to the cause of the accident; this, since that had generally been found to be the case in attempts to utilise this "type of classificatory system" as an aid to the "understanding of human behavior". In discussing the 'behavioural model' and the 'epidemiological model', Suchman (1961:248) offered that the approaches are "not incompatible, but differ in the relative emphasis they place on the degree of human control".

Despite these warnings and the existence of evidence that was contrary to notions of multi-causality, many practitioners, academics and writers erroneously held on to Gordon's ideas. But, as regards the application of his original 'triad' in certain medical areas, most had found it to be "lacking" (Thomas et al 2003). As a result, epidemiology moved on to causal chains and then on again into the still deeper and ever more complex ground of the "web of causation" (McMahon et al 1960). Not surprisingly, many practitioners and writers of the day followed suit (e.g. Grose 1987) and quickly added management into the already unsubstantiated equation (i.e. host, agent, environment, management). Indeed, later writers such as Reason (1997:2004) have gone further and fully incorporated medical, psychological and epidemiologically flavoured language into their writings. However, the move into deeper complexity by epidemiologists is suspected as being due to a preoccupation with intricately modelling risk rather than understanding its origins and implications. For Krieger (1994:899), the widespread multivariate approach to theory encouraged by metaphor of the 'web of causation' is "deeply flawed".

Metaphors, Myths and the Effective Denial of Human Behaviour

In 1970, (in a rare manuscript insofar as the advice of the relevant editorial board was that it be accepted without revision), Suchman (1970:4) reported that the search for causes had remained focussed on environmental factors and that control programs had largely concentrated on "eliminating or safety-proofing physical hazards". However, and fully recognising the importance and need to install such controls, he reported that *"accidental injuries and death continue to occur regardless of such environmental controls"*. Beyer (1916) and Heinrich (1941) had drawn the same conclusions and so has the most modern of such studies, the TYS. In addition, a warning shot was fired across the UK regulator's bows for instance by Lord Robens (Cmnd 5034:9) where the report of his committee offered that...

"We have now reached a state where many of the causes of serious accidents which were once common have been brought under control, at least in most places most of the time. Methods of guarding have been greatly improved...a very large number of the accidents which can readily be prevented by physical means are now prevented...yet reported accidents continue to rise".

Noted earlier, the Factory Inspectors of the day were adamant that additional legislation was not the answer; indeed, analysis of the relevant reports points clearly to an on-going awareness of behavioural problems (Difford 2004). Closer to present day, an HSE research report had this to say...

"In recent years the nature of accident causation has changed with engineering failures no longer being a major feature in many accidents.

It is now largely behavioural with human failings being a significant part of the causes of most accidents. Of these, knowingly deviating from approved work practice represents a large proportion of incidents involving some form of human error. This form of human error is often termed 'violation'." (HSE 2002:1).

Whilst it is refreshing to see that the HSE have at least been made aware of the error /violation problem, the report is wrong to say that the problem has only emerged "in recent years". Contrary to that part of the statement and the views of many (e.g. Reason et al 2006: Hollnagel 2008), we have seen more than enough evidence above to say that the nature of risk has not changed in the past 80 years and neither have the causes of it materialising.

As regards their efforts to move certain aspects forward, the work of authors such as Petersen and Bird & Loftus are commendable. That said, the results of their efforts cannot be measured (Swuste 2008: HSE 2005) and so any commendation here is for effort, not result. On the other hand, at least one effect of their efforts *is* obvious. They have created problems for analysis by way of their belief that a multi-faceted interrogation of the systems that they promote will reveal the cause of an accident and, hence, its remedy. However, they serve, by way of identifying conditions, to tell us about factors that are *"associated with accidents"*, but not what are causing them (Suchman 1961:250). For many (Suchman: Heinrich 1941: 1959: TYS), the answer resides in the field of social psychology and human behaviour; but, that has been confused with an all encompassing notion of ergonomics and human factors.

Official Publications – What are they Based on?

According to Difford (2004:), it is clear that the UK HSE for instance has no strategy for resolving the human behaviour problem. In 1989, the HSE released its principal offering on the subject by way of "HSG48: Human Factors in Industrial Safety" (subsequent editions being titled HSG48: Reducing Error and Influencing Behaviour").

Clear from the outset, HSG48 was based on what the HSE should have realised was an unproven (if not wholly flawed) multi-factoral, epidemiological approach (i.e. Organisation, Job/environment, Person). In addition, it was clear that the philosophy was based on the belief that compliance with traditional health and safety provisions would be enough to address the problem. However, in what should have been the critical areas, the publication imported the academic language from Reason (1990) and a bizarre qualifier in the 1st edition of HSG48 that "the classification system" that it outlines "*is open to debate*" (HSE 1989:5); interestingly (if not alarmingly), that qualification is absent in subsequent editions!

According to the 1999 and 2009:(p11) editions, latent failures (i.e. Reason's latent conditions) are "*made by people*" and are "*typically failures in health and safety management systems*". Whilst most would agree with the first part (at least until the true nature of the latent condition is identified later below), it is, of course, the second part that is disputed here; indeed, the HSE have no basis whatsoever for any such statement and to say that it is misleading is an understatement. Furthermore, the unnecessary and erroneous causative link suggested by HSG48 from people failures to system failures fully bears out the earlier suggestion that the latent failure or condition is a synonym for root cause; that said, it is a relatively easy statement for the HSE to make since neither they nor the Crown are generally required to prove causation during a prosecution.

The full extent of the TYS review of HSG48 and other HSE guidance etc is unimportance here. However, later editions of HSG48 contain a modified version of a diagram by Reason (1990:207) that he aptly referred to as the '*psychological varieties of unsafe acts*'. HSG48 modified the diagram and the 'types' of violation that can occur and re-titled it as 'types of human failure'. As a result, clear from analysis of both HSG48 and HSG65, *any* violation can now be subjectively attributed to management (which is generally the case during prosecutions of course). Yet, HSG48 is fully aware of the following...

"Individual characteristics influence behaviour in complex and significant ways. Their effects on task performance may be negative and may not always be mitigated by job design'. (HSE 2009:5).

In addition, via L21, the HSE and HSG48 are also fully aware of the fact that...

"Adverse events such as an accident, ill health or dangerous occurrence may take place even if a suitable and sufficient risk assessment has been made and appropriate preventive and protective measures taken" (HSE 2007:16).

However, and as we know in cases where no management failure can be found, the only advice from the HSE is to 'review the risk assessment'. But, and whilst attention to legal and system requirements is absolutely necessary, a constant polishing of the filing cabinet and a re-juggling of the risk control paperwork that it contains is not addressing *the* causes of accidents. As a result, notions of circularity and tail-chasing leap uncontrollably to mind and both behaviour and violation are left unaddressed. In the critical area needing attention (i.e. remedies for those accidents that are caused solely by individual behaviour, despite a fully compliant system), HSG48 has no answer. The document has taken it upon itself to adjust an academic's work in order to reinforce its own equally unsubstantiated view that management cause all accidents; this, despite its 'own' research to the contrary. The critical areas that industry needs assistance with, not least the difficult task of guarding against violation HSE (1998), are conveniently side-stepped and the one document that should have helped becomes but another obstacle to prevention. Its 'fashionable' views on culture and attitudes are also highly debatable and out of step with many (McBroom & Reed 1992). In any event, the law makes the employer liable for behaviour...a totally different phenomenon.

In the main, HSG48 repeats information that can be found elsewhere (e.g. in HSG65 and L21) and, not least, encourages accident investigators and employers to...

'consider causes and contributing factors that are remote in time and space from the accident (often these will be decisions made by managers) as well as immediate causes (often these will be failures by 'front line' staff)" (HSE 2009b:44).

Whilst the "person responsible" may indeed be far removed from the scene (Heinrich & Lateiner 1969:218; TYS), the HSE's statement is aligned to its support for the term latent failure insofar as the 'person *causatively* responsible' will always, according to the HSE and Reason (1997), be a manager; hence, the organisation. However, the type of search encouraged by the HSE requires a trawl through the antecedent causal chain and, as a result, deliberate acts are ignored and nought but conditions are identified. Furthermore, its unnecessary and unexplained distinction between 'decisions' of managers and 'failures' of front line workers serves only to reinforce the management failure myth. Yet, neither the HSE nor Reason (1990:1997) had any empirical data upon which to suggest such a causative relationship between management and accidents; indeed, clear from everything thus far, the HSE holds far more contradictory evidence than supportive evidence. According to Difford (2004)...

"As long as operatives and practitioners believe that there is always going to be a root [management failure] cause, then there can be little hope of any front-line ownership or behavioural change...Whilst organisations are aware that there will be an automatic search for a management failure or root cause, defensive strategies and resistance to change (or to acknowledge that change is required) will result".

As it is, HSG48 can be referred to in a Court of law as being illustrative of 'good practice'. As such, the HSE is effectively able to present itself as an expert in the field of violation, human error and human behaviour. However, given the persistent prosecution failure rate (failures which show people, not systems, to be the cause), the HSE are either in denial of the role of human behaviour or are unaware of its true nature. As if to confuse industry further, HSG48 provides a list of further reading. Amongst the books suggested are Reason (1990) which is a book aimed primarily at academic cognitive psychologists (Reason et al 2006:4). It is also the book that contains, as the 1st edition of HSG48 puts it, a 'debatable' classification scheme. One of the other books recommended for further reading is Reason (1997). That book introduced the Swiss cheese model (SCM) and will be under the spotlight (if it isn't already) later below. That model, using terms like 'resident pathogen' (i.e. latent condition), has a multi-factoral epidemiological basis and has repeatedly shown itself to be flawed and unusable (TYS). Indeed, Reason (1990:198) offered that the terms he uses are *"unacceptably vague"* and that the *"resident pathogen metaphor"* *"is far from being a workable theory"*. Consequently, someone might consider taking the HSE seriously to the task of explaining why they are recommending such reading to industry; notwithstanding that the HSE's own reason for supporting it should be obvious to all but the most naive.

Parliamentary Office of Science and Technology

Unfortunately, the TYS found that it is not just industry and the safety profession that have succumbed to academic invention. For instance...

*"POST is an office of both houses of [the UK] Parliament, charged with providing **independent and balanced analysis** of public policy issues that have a basis in science and technology"* (Parliament 2001:8).

In June 2001, it released a Postnote (PN156) entitled "Managing Human Error" that contained, not surprisingly perhaps, a diagram of Reason's SCM. However, and far from producing any "independent" or "balanced analysis" of it, PN156 merely regurgitated Reason's (1990:2000) own uttering's on the model. Indeed, it was clear that the author of the document (funded by the British Psychological Society) had not the slightest understanding of the SCM beyond its own propaganda. In consequence, the document has unwittingly incorporated numerous biases and assumptions.

Whilst the regurgitation of the SCM's own propaganda is understandable given that few research centres on the planet are capable of analysing it properly, there is no excuse for reproducing inaccuracies. For some reason, PN156 opted to discuss the capsizing of the Herald of Free Enterprise. In its discussion, PN156:5 stated that the "top-heavy design" of the vessel was one of a number of *"design failures"* implicated in the disaster. However, and despite referencing the official report into the disaster, it did not take its comment from there since no such comment exists within it. Indeed, the inaccuracy came directly from Reason (1990:256) who believes that the Herald's "top heavy design" was a *latent failure* (i.e. latent condition or resident pathogen) that made the vessel "inherently unsafe".

Whilst the UK HSE may have questionable reason to support the SCM philosophy, the Parliamentary Office of Science and Technology claims to be independent. Consequently, it should be ensuring that its publications are subjected to properly independent and objective review prior to release; as regards PN156's statement regarding the Herald and, more importantly here, on the matter of the SCM, that has not been the case.

INTERIM SUMMARY

Gordon's (1949) assumption that the factors of host, agent and environment combine *to cause* accidents was wrong; in addition, it was, and remains to be, contrary to all empirical data in the relevant domains. Even in the domain to which it should have been confined, it was found lacking. Indeed, Suchman had specifically warned that such models or methods would only reveal things that were *"indirectly related"* to the accident in question and later experts confirmed that epidemiology cannot assist with causation in individual cases.

Later, epidemiology moved on to causal chains and then causal nets or webs. However, the new multivariate approach was seen by many to be deeply flawed. As is the case with supporters of multiple causation such as Hollnagel and Reason who came after Petersen, the tendency has been towards confused and apparently complex modelling rather than coherent statements on causation that express a defensible understanding of the true nature of risk and the way that it materialises; of course, the true nature of risk has *never* changed.

Nonetheless, many saw epidemiology as having provided some sort of validity to their belief in multiple causation and, also without any form of data driven support, quickly added management into the equation. However, the notion that man, machine, management and environment combine to cause accidents is a fallacious myth. Suchman and Lord Robens both presented evidence which confirmed that attention to the numerous factors comprising the working environment was not preventing accidents; indeed, Suchman made it clear that causes do not lie within such factors...men cause accidents. In the context here, epidemiology provides no support whatsoever to multiple causation theory or similar multi-facetted notions of cause.

Whilst the UK HSE for instance allude to be assisting industry with the behavioural problem, their offerings are nothing more than poorly disguised instructions to continue with the flogging of the same old dead horse; even when the horse in question has clearly done nothing wrong. Embracing the fallacy of epidemiology in the industrial domain and the incoherent ramblings of largely inexperienced academics, they continually dip industry, sheep like, into the abyss of the metaphorical. In full support of Reason (1990:1997:2004), they have continually sought to convince industry that upstream managers (hence, the organisation) will always be the proximate cause of accidents. However, and whilst that is contrary to the evidence that they actually hold, the only basis for any such belief or instruction to industry is by way of unworkable theory, unacceptably vague metaphor and the knowingly debatable. That said, the reason that they should want to hold on to that belief might be a far more appropriate explanation for some to seek.

Chapter Five Part 1:
The Start of the Management Failure Movement

Soundly established basic principles must withstand tampering, not withstanding the natural temptation to discard the old, adopt the new, and to change merely for the sake of change. (Heinrich 1959:xi).

Weaver's (1971) Accident Sequence

Earlier above, we noted that Petersen (1971) had said in his preface that D. A. Weaver helped him to develop many, if not all, of the thoughts in his book. Consequently, Weaver's (1971) accident sequence is depicted below at Fig. was1.

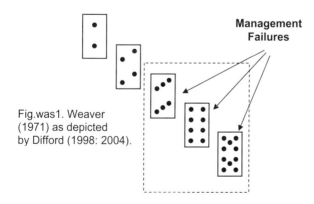

Fig.was1. Weaver (1971) as depicted by Difford (1998: 2004).

Domino 1. is titled Social Environmental and Heredity.

Domino 2. is titled Personal Failings or Mistakes.

Domino 3. is titled Unsafe Behaviour/Physical Hazard.

Domino 4. is titled Accident.

Domino 5. is titled Injury - Property Damage - Near-miss.

Weaver's accident sequence sees dominoes 3., 4. and 5. as being 'symptoms of operational error'. At a stretch, initially, the placing of responsibility for *all* 'unsafe acts' upon the shoulders of management would be morally acceptable. However, Weaver's sequence is based on Petersen's (1971) notion of multiple causation (Cooper 2001) and, as a result, the proximate or root causes of *all* accidents become management failures (Wiegmann & Shappell 2003:39); clearly, that is a step too far. Responsibility for an accident, whether morally or in the eyes of the law, is one thing; but, a default assumption that such responsibility equates automatically to cause... that's something else.

Like Petersen, Weaver provided nothing by way of any analysis or data that might lend even the remotest of support to what is otherwise a mere notion or idea. Of course, Weaver was instrumental in Petersen putting forward his notion of multiple causation and so it is fair to say that Weaver's sequence and multiple causation theory gain support only from each other; that is, they fuel, in a wholly circular fashion, one another's otherwise unsupportable beliefs. Furthermore, given that we must now consider things from a systems perspective, there was no mechanism by which the so called root cause could be verified. Indeed, the model ignores yet another system requirement insofar as there is essentially no need to verify the effectiveness of any remedy that results.

A central theme of such models is that they reject the common cause hypothesis in preference for the notion that all accidents are different.

Consequently, when the next accident occurs in otherwise identical circumstances, it is easy to defend the previous remedy (even though it has been totally ineffective) by stating that this 'new' accident is different. However, according to Difford (1998: 2004), there is no such thing as a 'new accident' since he feels that they have all happened before. Similarly, Grose (1987:188) believes that there are "no totally new" risks. Whilst those statements might seem outlandish to some, they stand up to logical tests. Indeed, given the ultimate causal destination of this book, those statements are undeniable.

Staying with Grose (1987) for a moment we might recall that he was noted earlier above in Chapter One as having stated (early in his book) *"that nearly all accidental losses have multiple causes"*. However, the qualification attached to that statement later disappears and he offers that "no accident has a singular cause" (p182). Referring to a diagram of six dominoes, he offers that accidents are "a series of human acts, decisions, or omissions" (p184). Consequently, and as a result, he goes on to conclude that "all dominoes are ultimately traceable to "human error"." (p199). In addition, and of similar interest and importance, Bamber (1996:169) confirms that each of the "multicauses" in multiple causation theory are "equivalent to the third domino in the Heinrich theory". So, before moving on, and to clarify this last paragraph; Grose and Bamber are confirming that only people can cause accidents and that all causal sequences reduce, logically post-accident, to linear or normative depictions (of course, the problem for many academics and writers arises from their inability to recognise which one of the errors has been causal in the transitive sense). Furthermore, it should be obvious that Weaver essentially reproduced Heinrich's sequence and made a causative statement in relation to management that was pure invention; indeed, it should have been challenged and rejected upon its very release.

Bird's (1974 Updated 'domino' Sequence

A few years after Weaver's model came Bird's (1974) 'updated domino sequence' (see Fig. bus1.). Recall from the earlier discussion above that Bird & Loftus (1976) considered that this update was necessary in order to...

*"reflect the direct management relationship involved with the causes of **all** incidents that could downgrade a business operatio*n".

Recall also that nothing was offered by way of support for this sequence either. As a result, and far from being 'outgrowths' of Heinrich's theory, all of the models to have emerged since are in stark contrast to it. Heinrich's findings (consistent with the TYS) were supported by analogy, experience and observation; three vitally important requirements (Hume 1772). Of course, none of the models that have emerged since Heinrich's had any such necessary support; indeed, from what we know and have already seen, it should be clear that such support was, in fact, impossible.

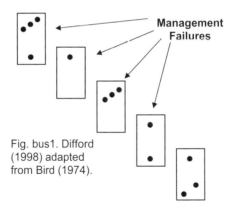

Fig. bus1. Difford (1998) adapted from Bird (1974).

Bird, who also formally introduced the notion of *contributory or causal factors* into the equation for purposes here, generally describes his dominoes as follows;

Domino or Factor 1.
...is titled Lack of Management Control.

This domino is now firmly identified as the starting place for all accident sequences (a view and philosophy that would later be mirrored by Reason's (1997) Swiss Cheese model). According to Bird, it will only fall when there is a lack of control by management; i.e. a lack of planning, organising, leading or controlling (Bird 1974:20-21).

Domino or Factor 2.
...is titled Basic Cause-Origin.

This domino relates to what Bird calls personal factors (e.g. knowledge, motivation, physical or mental problems) and job factors (e.g. inadequate design, maintenance, work or purchasing standards). The assumption is that when domino 1. falls (i.e. the first management failure; or, in SCM parlance, the first barrier failure), there will be an additional management failure waiting to accommodate it and produce the accident.

Whilst a causal (i.e. normative or linear) chain is clearly, and quite correctly, emerging and being implied, we will see shortly below and later that Bird, as with Reason and his SCM, are compelled to deny the normative depiction since multiple causation theory (hence, the SCM) would, categorically and irrefutably, disprove itself if it were to support it.

Domino or Factor 3.
...is titled Immediate Cause-Symptom.

This domino relates to substandard practices, conditions, errors and violations and is essentially the same as Heinrich's domino number 3. However, all unsafe conditions, no matter how they arise, have been assigned to management as have all forms of error and violation, including those of supervisors (again, Reason's Swiss Cheese model mirrors this). Whilst here, Bird's list of unsafe practices is worth noting in full;

- Operating without authority.

- Failure to warn or secure.

- Operating at improper speed.

- Making safety devices inoperable.

- Using defective equipment.

- Using equipment improperly.

- Failure to use personal protective equipment.

- Improper loading or placement.

- Improper lifting.

- Taking improper position.

- Servicing equipment in motion.

- Horseplay.

- Drinking or drugs.

Whilst fully acknowledging that unsafe acts, errors and violations occur, Bird's view is that all of these result solely from management failures. He says...

'whether we refer to these deviations as substandard practices and conditions or unsafe acts and conditions, there is one important thing common to all. Each and every one is only a symptom of the basic cause that permitted the practices or conditions to exist. When we fail to determine what the basic causes behind the symptoms really are, we fail to keep this domino from falling, and the direct potential for loss exists' (Bird 1974:23).

According to Bird (1974) and Bird & Loftus (1976), and noting that the above list is far from exhaustive, everything identified on it are 'symptoms' of dominoes 1. & 2. Effectively, it presumes a workplace full of mindless automatons devoid of free will and common sense such that, regardless of what anyone does, it will always be someone else's fault (i.e. attributable, ultimately and without exception, to management or the organisation). However, 35 years on, we can see that most items on the list remain to be appropriate today in workplaces where everything required by the law and the system is, in fact, *in place*. On just the last bullet point alone, some organisations informed the TYS that they had either suspended, or were considering suspending, random drugs and alcohol tests due to 'hit rates' as high as 23-29% (the problem was particularly rife in the maritime, heavy engineering and construction sectors). Of course, no organisation is safe; for instance, cocaine was *again* found at NASA's Florida Space Centre in March 2011 (cocaine having also been found in January 2010 in a secure part of a hangar that housed the Space Shuttle Discovery) (*source* Independent). If organisations or readers are surprised then they ought not to be since it has long been known that man works as he lives (Suchman 1970:6 citing McFarland 1966) and there is little that an employer can do about the latter (HSE 1998:38; Reason 1990:206). That said, organisations and readers *should* be surprised at the acknowledgements of this by the UK HSE and Reason; indeed, they should be stunned given the HSE's and Reason's belief that management are the sole cause of worker behaviour.

Of course, most of the behaviours identified in Bird's list above actually tend to occur during periods of self-supervision. That said, they often occur in full sight of other employees as well (TYS); where that is the case, at risk and negative behaviour becomes condoned on a group basis (however, note that this book is not the place to take that discussion further and the useable output of TYS research in that field will be presented by Difford in a later text: see Appendix 2).

Domino or Factor 4.
...is titled Incident-Contact. (i.e. the accident or near-miss).

I have said 'accident' here since those who use the word 'incident' when accident is clearly required should question their reasons for using it; alternatively, they should question the motives of those who require them to use it since it is a potentially damaging and blame-laden term.

Domino or Factor 5.
...is tilted People-Property-Loss. (i.e. injury, damage or loss).

Before moving on, it should be noted from Fig. bus1. above that Bird's 'dominoes' contain random spots or 'holes'; that is, they *are not* sequentially numbered dominoes. At first sight, the model appears to show a linear or normative cause-effect sequence; but, that is an impossibility for models such as this and Reason's (1997) SCM that are based on notions of multi-causality; not least, it is an impossibility for any (e.g. Petersen, Bird or Reason) who believe that *all* accidents are different. Sooner or later, authors of such models are compelled to recognise that fact but the recognition never comes by way of the statement that is actually required; for instance, in relation to Bird's sequence, Bird & Loftus (1976:50) offered this...

"Re-emphasis is directed to the fact that the domino effect is not necessarily a direct chain reaction involved with single events. It is rather a reaction involving the potential of multiple events at each stage, with each established causal factor capable of continuing the reaction itself and of interacting with other factors to continue the domino effect".

The random nature of the spots or holes is a necessity since such models have no predictive capability whatsoever. That said, such models insist that management, *invariably and unconditionally*, cause *all* accidents. However, that prophecy can only be fulfilled in retrospect. Furthermore, it can only be fulfilled if the investigator is forced to backtrack beyond the limit of the properly over-lapping or transitive causes that are otherwise logically identified by the unsafe act (more properly referred to as the deliberate act). That forcing itself is apparently justified by the checklists (i.e. lists of safety indicators or audit or inspection categories) that such models compel investigators to use. However, such forcing compels the identification of nothing more than conditions; consequently, for now, I will say that a high degree of ignorance, concoction and manipulation is evidenced by the use of such models.

Accident Prone or Error Prone?

According to Wiegmann & Shappell (2003:38-39), Bird's is "perhaps the best known organizational model of human error". They see this and Weaver's 'model' as having *"described the cascading nature of human error beginning with the failure of management to control losses"*. That said, and not surprisingly, they quickly add that just "exactly how management" causes all this error is "often difficult to put your finger on"; of course, they do not offer any elaboration on how management cause the errors that they *could*, supposedly, put their finger on. In any event, Difford (2004) argues that those models *describe* no such thing and that Wiegmann & Shappell's view of them as organisational models of human error is their own invention; according to him, Wiegmann & Shappell do nothing more than confirm that all accidents stem from human behaviour. Indeed, he sees Bird's model as an extreme and damaging one given, not least, that it alluded to be following Heinrich's work. By virtue of dominoes one, two and three, an accident in a totally compliant workplace full of totally competent men can only be due to a management or organisational failure; what's more, the 'model' purports to show this causatively. For Difford (2004), the notions of the so-called organisational accident (Reason 2004) (discussed later below) and the organisational model of human error are pure fictions. They rely largely, if not exclusively, on the belief that workers have neither right, inclination, ability nor opportunity to exercise free will in the workplace. However, not only was that suggestion disputed by every Director, Senior Manager and HR professional spoken to during the TYS, it is also contrary to the views of both expert (O'Connor 1995: Botham 2008) and layman (TYS).

In reality, hundreds of the deaths analysed by the TYS were found to be due solely to the fact that the relevant individual *had* exercised free will. Similarly, in thousands of instances where a prosecution for a fatality had either failed or was considered inappropriate, the conclusion can only be the same. The earlier reference above to Hale & Perusse (1977) also showed that workers are adamant in their belief that both they and their colleagues have, and do exercise, free will; 93% of 2200 worker respondents agreed (TYS). To deny free will is to contradict the common man's view of things as well as numerous studies (e.g. HSE 2002: 2004a: 2004b: 2004c).

Again, there is absolutely no notion of blame here whatsoever; this book should be encouraging readers to at least pause for a moment and consider the basis of their views on the causes of accidents. Nonetheless, it suits some to deny the natural phenomenon that is free-will; indeed, given the premise of their theories, some are compelled to deny it. But, if we consider and accept (even if only temporarily) that workers have free-will, then we have to accept that they cause things to happen as free agents. As such, we must accept that they are sometimes the sole cause of an accident rather than some hapless pawn that is but a passive component in some complex and wider causal sequence of events (Botham 2008). As O'Connor (1995) suggests, when 'B' causes 'C' we sometimes have to accept that the cause of 'C' was nothing more than 'B' himself and that no other relevant cause (i.e. transitive cause) exists in the upstream antecedent causal chain. Consequently, those who would touch upon matters related to free will might bear in mind that, when they do so, they enter the realm of the philosopher. As such, they might be guided by a word or two of wisdom...

"...in things that are within the reach of every man's understanding, and upon which the whole conduct of human life turns, the philosopher must follow the multitude, or make himself perfectly ridiculous" (Reid 1764).

Accident proneness (more intelligible perhaps if viewed as *error* proneness since we are all (Kohn et al 2003), directors etc included (HSE 1998), prone to *err*) also gets quickly introduced and disposed of by the 'no free will' school (a disposal, according to Visser et al 2007, that could be in error; indeed, even Reason (2004:129) concedes that error prone people do exist). But, and similar to the denial of free will, does it allow the side-stepping of a question that might otherwise be unanswerable? For instance, we know that many organisations report certain groups (sometimes individuals) as having higher 'incident' rates than others. That said, some have found that the majority of serious outcome accidents are actually suffered by experienced workers with no real previous accident history at all (Greenwood & Wood 1953: the TYS agreed but with a qualifier on the term 'accident'). Consequently, the question for those who support the view that workers have 'no free will' and that none are accident (error) prone is simple; in either case, how can the organisation and its systems be simultaneously responsible for the achievement and non-achievement of safety? That is, how can it protect an individual one minute but, not the next; or, what is it that could possibly single out one worker for injury whilst the rest of the workforce (apparently waiting their turn for an accident) look on unaffected? Of course, we wouldn't be asking such questions at all but for the tendency in some, contrary to available information, logic and commonsense, to view all error and violation as but 'symptoms' of organisational (or more correctly, someone else's) failings.

The insight (as opposed to preferred, contrary and imaginary explanations) that industry needs into error is obstructed by those (e.g. Reason 2004:126; Woods et al 2010) who see unsafe acts as "consequences" of organisational failings. But, where death, major-injury or environmental damage (whether it effects the individual directly concerned, or an aeroplane or a ship or a patient) results from an act or omission, the proximate cause is never of Bird's managerial or Reason's organisational type. At a stretch, error is behaviour (Bogner 2004) but, it is not a system driven phenomenon insofar as it has not been found to be caused by the environment in the academic, epidemiological or multi-factoral sense (TYS). More often than not, it results from an individual's assessment of the environment's ability to either prevent or support the behaviour that they are contemplating (Ajzen 1991); e.g. in a similar way to which a 'speed camera' might have a temporary effect on driving behaviour whilst the presence of a certain passenger in the vehicle might have a more longer lasting effect (positive or negative). Nonetheless, many, devoid of workable and measurable solutions, will arbitrarily assign the cause of error to the organisation; that said, and whilst it mirrors the SCM, Bogner's (2004) bizarrely titled "systems approach artichoke model of error" believes in a cause beyond the organisation. But, where an 'unsafe act' has been objectively and unbiasedly attributed to behaviour then, far more often than not, its cause has been factually attributed to the person directly involved...not fictionally attributed to the organisation and its systems.

"If all human agency is ultimately just a matter of one event's causing another, then, since the causal history of the events supposedly involved in any instance of human agency will plausibly be traceable back, through prior events, to times before the agent's birth, we seem to lose all sense of the agent's being genuinely responsible for...his or her own actions. A human agent must then be seen as no freer, in reality, than the boulder which rolls into the tree, its rolling being caused by the action of some other object upon it, which action is in turn caused by yet earlier events-and so on back to the dawn of time". (Lowe 2002:201-2).

Viewed reasonably and objectively, the notion that at risk behaviour is a *symptom* of multiple upstream organisational failures is clearly wrong. Furthermore, the definition of a *symptom* as applied by those who would seek to utilise such epidemiological terms is also wrong. In an injury producing accident for instance, it would be the injury itself that is the *symptom* as far as accident prevention is concerned. Therefore, an injury is symptomatic of 'someone's' at risk or unsafe behaviour (whether of the person directly involved or of some other). As such, it is the injury producing behaviour that must be understood if we are to improve the prediction and control of a future accident (Suchman 1961). It therefore follows, obviously, that a focus of attention on the injury would tell us nothing about the cause of the accident. Similarly, moving away upstream to senior management in search of cause is just as futile since the critical element, the behaviour of the person proximately involved, is effectively removed from the equation.

If an accident has been caused by an organisational or management failure (whatever that is since I have never seen one myself) then a professional investigator *will* discover it and advise accordingly on appropriate remedial intervention strategies. What he will not do is to presume it and go looking for it, especially in sight of clear evidence to the contrary. Unfortunately, whilst current philosophies persist, the remedy will continue to be outside of the system's ability to protect either the organisation or the individual from it. Consequently, I will utilise Newton (1687) here and say that we should...

Admit no more causes of natural things than as are both true and sufficient to explain their appearances. Therefore, to the same natural effects we must, so far as is possible, assign the same causes.

Questionable Use of 'research' by the Regulator

Whilst models such as Bird's contain no mechanism by which the root and other so called 'causal factors' can be verified (and, hence, how any correlation has been logically identified and determined), they are content to imply a multi-facetted causal relationship. However, when the findings of such have been objectively tested, the relationships tend to be spurious. Nonetheless, Bird's model (later marketed under the banner of the *total loss approach*) was instrumental in furthering the belief that multiple management failures causatively underlie all accidents (TYS); a belief, not surprisingly perhaps, that was also attractive to certain regulatory authorities.

In the UK for instance, the Health & Safety Executive were quick to adopt Bird's (1974) language and beliefs. In 'Successful Health & Safety Management' (HSG65), a leading publication, it announced that "Accidents are caused by the absence of adequate management control" (HSE 1991:9; 1997a). Relying predominantly and erroneously on Bird's (1974) *'accident triangle'* (see fig. bp2.), it stated that "the total loss approach is based on research into accident causation". However, that was both misleading and inaccurate;

indeed, Difford (2004) declared it to be an appalling publication evidencing an appalling waste of public funds.

Fig bp2.

Bird (1974)

Bird's triangle, following a claimed analysis of 1,753,498 accidents, makes neither reference nor allusion to cause. Along exactly the same lines as Heinrich's triangle it identifies a set of severity ratios and an estimation of near-misses (Bird 1974: Bird & Loftus 1976), *and that is all*. Consequently, it must be remembered that Bird's 'updated domino sequence' is in no way related to his triangle; his updated sequence is but his own, erroneous notion of cause. Whilst Bird & Loftus (1976) offered that "gaining new insight into human behaviour presents one of the greatest challenges in the field of loss prevention", they quickly moved away from that key issue. The principal theorem supporting the total loss approach for purposes here was that "accidents and other losses are largely the result of inadequate management performance in safety or loss control work". However, that statement, which remains to be wholly and wildly inaccurate, was not supported by any type of data, information or empirical research; despite which, HSG 65 (HSE 1991:9) would state that...

"Accidents, ill-health and incidents...generally arise from failures in control and often have multiple causes".

A few years later, the statement underwent a subtle but significant change to...

"Accidents, ill-health and incidents...generally arise from failures of control and involve multiple contributory elements" (HSE 1997a: 2000: 2003e: 2009a:14).

Also undergoing change in the 1997, 2000, 2003e and 2009 versions of HSG65 was the statement regarding the total loss approach having been based on research into *accident causation*. According to those later versions, it was now based on research into the *causes of accidents* (e.g. HSE 1997:7). Of course, both statements were wrong and the latter was particularly misleading.

Such changes have far reaching implications since they suggest that research has been conducted into *actual* accidents in order to determine *actual* causes. Furthermore, they suggest that research and empirical evidence exists that presents absolute proof regarding both the existence and the role of the so-called multiple causes or contributory factors. Consequently, they purport to be authoritatively identifying both cause and remedy. However, analysis of the relevant work, which included analysis of certain research conducted by and for the HSE, revealed absolutely nothing upon which such statements could factually be made. Indeed, the overwhelming weight of evidence passed to the HSE via its research reports is to the contrary; in fact, the HSE alone possesses an abundance of information that is not only contrary to the principal theorem upon which the 'total loss approach' is based but, disproves multiple causation theory as well.

Nonetheless, and already noted above, the HSE have continually advised industry and the safety profession that management are responsible for about 70% of accidents. However, relevant interviews and research during the TYS revealed that the only possible basis for the 70% figure is by way of analogy to 'prosecution success' rates; which, presents numerous problems.

As we know, the vast majority of prosecution successes come by way of guilty pleas. But, when the TYS made reasonable adjustments for negotiation and 'plea bargaining', the shock that some businesses undergo at the time and the pressure applied by insurers to reduce costs, a question mark appears over the validity (causation wise) of many guilty pleas and, hence, certain so-called prosecution successes. In addition, we know that the prosecution does not have to prove cause (*R* v *Chargot*) and in many instances (e.g. *R* v *Nelson*: *R* v *HTM*) would be totally unable to. Furthermore, we know that the HSE has not been in the habit of pursuing 'all reasonable lines of enquiry', especially those that 'could assist the defence' (HSE W1) (recall that no evidence has been found to indicate that this stance has changed). Therefore, the fact that there has been a successful criminal prosecution and/or the fact that a duty holder has 'decided' to plead guilty does not enable an automatic assumption that there has been any factual finding or belief in the duty holder's role *causatively*.

Unfortunately, the problem is made worse where the Institutions that examine and professionally qualify safety practitioners (certainly in the UK) are apparently aligned, 'politically' perhaps, to the regulatory perspective (TYS). The study found, and continues to find, an alarming tendency in safety practitioners to address their employer's or client's investigations with the 'mind-set' of the regulator; that is, they are seeking breaches, not causes. In addition, from a reasonable sampling, the TYS estimated that at least 30% of convicted organisations were advised, wrongly, to plead guilty on nothing more than the 'verdict' of the in-house safety advisor.

Clearly, from just this small section alone, the HSE has nothing whatsoever upon which to base the view that either management or systems deficiencies are causing a majority of accidents. If the section is wrong, where is the data resulting from the causal analysis of the 30% of fatalities that management were apparently unable to prevent? That, surely, is what the preventionist needs since, firstly, it presents proof positive that men are killing themselves (perhaps by exercising free will) in workplaces that are in full compliance with the law; indeed, killing themselves in workplaces that have robust systems and policies in place. Secondly, it would present additional insight into whatever it is that is currently beyond the reach of existing laws, systems and causal philosophies; insight, that is, into how a system can possibly be both effective and ineffective, simultaneously.

As it is, and far from providing solutions, the HSE view is both circular, illogical and contradictory; as are the models that share such views (e.g. Reason's Swiss Cheese, Petersen's multiple causation and Bird's updated sequence). In one sense, according to HSG65, all immediate and underlying causes stem from a failure to devise and implement an adequate safety policy (HSE 2009a:87); nonsensically, that includes the 30% of accidents that management and the system were not responsible for according to the courts. In such cases, the HSE's (2007) advice is to review the risk assessment; but, what is the point if it has already been found to be adequate? Indeed, (noting that the TYS found that it is impossible even for an absent risk assessment itself to be a root cause) what is the point given that one study commissioned by the HSE concluded that "sub-standard" risk assessments were not a "fundamental source of risk in many incidents" (HSE 2006:1).

Lord Young's (Iosh 2009) view that health and safety, "in crisis", is "at best an object of ridicule and at worse a bureaucratic nightmare" could be correct. But, if the TYS is correct, the source of the problem and the stereotyping of safety practitioners in the UK at least is the HSE, the leading professional body and the principal examination board (NEBOSH); not the practitioners who are mere reflections of them. Williams (2011) offers that Cameron (2009) (current 'UK' prime minister) is right to say that the 'cause of the excessive health and safety culture' is due to the way in which the laws are interpreted. But, he says that Cameron has removed the focus of attention away from the 'effective' interpreters (i.e. the HSE, Iosh and NEBOSH). If that is correct, any industrial solutions will be ineffective since they are bound to have incorporated the major part of the current problem. Indeed, and whilst politics has no place here, the problem should not be understated. According to the UK Law Commission, during its deliberations of causation and corporate killing, the Health & Safety Executive informed it that...

"...in practice the negligence of a single individual was rarely the sole cause of death or personal injury, which were generally the result of failure in systems for controlling risk, the carelessness of an individual

or individuals being a (more or less important) contributory factor".
(Law Comm No. 237:90)

Clearly, the HSE were not in a position to make such a statement and there are no doubt some who might feel that it was knowingly incorrect; for certain, the HSE should have known that it was incorrect. In any event, as regards the essential matter in hand here, it can be fairly stated that HSG65 contains unsubstantiated, misleading and irresponsible statements.

Before moving on, reference was made earlier to *R* v *HTM* and it is a pertinent case upon which to conclude this part. In 1999, a revision to the UK's Management of Health and Safety at Work Regulations was released which, at Regulation 21, says this...

"Nothing in the relevant statutory provisions shall operate so as to afford an employer a defence in any criminal proceedings for a contravention of those provisions by reason of any act or default of –

(a) an employee of his, or

(b) a person appointed by him under regulation 7." (Regulation 7. requires an employer to obtain health & safety assistance to assist compliance with his duties).

Central to the case of *R* v *HTM* was the Crown's failed attempt to invoke regulation 21. as a means to prevent the defence from relying on information and instruction that had been given to two employees (both of whom had tragically died in an accident).

Firstly, the Court of Appeal ruling that the Crown could not use regulation 21. in the way that it wanted was a land mark decision for those of us who work in the real world. If the decision had gone the other way then the criminal courts would have effectively been sanctioning the view that all errors and violations are caused by management; individual responsibility, training and so on would amount to nothing.

However, that the HSE and the Crown should need to reduce itself to such tactics was saddening. For some, the failure of the Crown's case in general was even more tragic and saddening. According to Difford (2nd TYS interim) it highlighted a serious flaw in investigative skills and an absence of understanding of the critical areas of law that applied in the relevant domain and the way that compliance with them should materialise in practice. He says that the inability of the HSE, its investigators and experts to properly assist the Crown prosecutor was a wake up call.

INTERIM SUMMARY

Despite Heinrich's warning, soundly established basic principles have been tampered with...incompetently. The result, models that have incorporated a misunderstanding (and, consequently, a misapplication) of epidemiology and the completely flawed notion of multiple causation. Worse still, in stark contradiction of Heinrich's work and all available data, the models claim to show management as being causatively responsible for all accidents. However, no model or theory that has ever put forward any such assumption has ever been able to supply anything by way of support for what is, quite simply, a completely contrary and unsupportable whim or idea.

Bird, for purposes here, was the first to introduce the notion of the management failure. Whilst he had neither empirical nor logical basis for either that notion or the re-labelling of a Heinrich type sequence, he moved the focus of attention fully away from individual responsibility and behaviour; in effect, logically determinable cause was, arbitrarily and by default, by-passed. Bird's belief, maintained by later writers who also have no answer to the human error and violation problem, was that man is neither causative of, nor responsible for, his own behaviour...ever. Whilst that is ridiculous to both worker and man in the street alike, it is also ridiculous to experts in that realm such as Lowe, O'Connor and Botham. Man, of course, regularly exercises free-will and his unsafe acts are not the consequences of organisational failings.

All dominoes and so-called multi-causes reduce, ultimately, to an unsafe act. Consequently, the real question is "how or why do academics and writers such as Bird believe that they can, invariably and unconditionally, engage in the impossible and allude to cause beyond that which logic and commonsense recognises and supports?" Indeed, why are the UK HSE amongst many who lend support to it?

Clearly, the advice offered to UK industry by the HSE (also utilised by many worldwide) in relation to cause is wrong. In fact, the HSE's view on cause is contrary to the data that it holds and is, therefore, knowingly wrong. Consequently, they are knowingly misleading industry and have also knowingly mislead the UK law Commission. If they are not doing this knowingly then they are expressing a level of incompetence that is beyond description here and is also one that is wholly at odds with any notion of public interest; indeed, nothing but self-interest springs to mind. Either way, the safety profession and industry should re-evaluate any perceived 'relationship' with it. The HSE/LA do not have to prove cause. Yet, they compel industry down an investigative path whereby it convinces itself, wholly erroneously, that it is the cause of all accidents. However, no member of the UK Law Commission, Crown Prosecution Service or any advisors to these would be able to support the HSE's view of cause. It represents, and supports, a ludicrously flawed notion of invariable and unconditional sequence to which we shall now turn.

Chapter Five Part 2:
A Notion of Cause that is Absurd both in Practice and in Principle

Not all Causes are Causes

To assist the points that need to be made here, we will consider *the cause* of a work shop fire. In describing things below and at Fig.cec1., dominoes are referred to. However, cabbages or footballs could just as easily have been used so do not allow them to confuse things. Additional information exists but, for purposes here, that can be introduced later below when we re-visit this example.

On the evening before the fire, X went to a football match and got home quite late. He suspects that he will be a little hung-over in the morning and so will decide then whether to go to work by car or bus. His employer operates a flexi-time schedule and so he can arrive for work half an hour either side of his standard starting times.

Domino 1.
X's alarm wakes him in the morning and he gets up.

Domino 2.
X goes through his normal routine and then goes to work by bus.

Domino 3:
CCTV footage of the smoking shelter at 17:55 shows one of X's colleagues discarding a newspaper onto the floor just prior to X

arriving. X arrives and lights a cigarette, discarding several matches directly onto the floor. Analysis reveals that the second of his discarded matches starts the paper smouldering. X does not realise this and leaves. He has been hanging around in order to make up the thirty minutes that he lost in the morning and is eventually the last man off site at 18:08 hrs.

Domino 4:
CCTV footage at 18:05 shows the smouldering newspaper being carried by the wind to some wooden pallets outside of the work shop. At 18:40, the pallets are alight. The fire spreads from the pallets and the work shop catches fire.

Domino 5:
Fire detectors in the work shop activate at 19:10 and an automated call is made to the fire brigade.

Domino 6:
A fire tender arrives at 19:20 and extinguishes the fire but the building is a total loss.

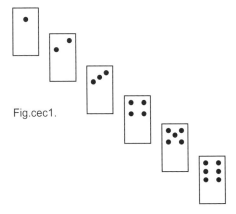

Fig.cec1.

Clearly, dominoes 1-6 are related in that they represent *at least one of the sequences* that the unwary might put forward as having culminated in the fire (I say *at least one of the sequences* since inexperience, or naivety, allows some to see numerous causal chains that each have numerous compositions available to them). However, if the antecedents at dominoes 1. & 2. are relevant then so too is the fact of the man's birth and the fact that his parents met by accident at a station owing to them having boarded wrong trains in 1952. As it happens, the cause of them boarding the wrong trains was their inability to understand the railway timetables of the day. Consequently, and whilst there are numerous 'causes' for the unwary to 'choose' from amidst such antecedents, it would not be completely ridiculous (insane and pointless maybe but not completely ridiculous) to cite either the wind or the complexity of railway timetables (60 years earlier) as being *the cause* since removal of either one from the equation would clearly have prevented the fire. Similarly, but for flexi-time, X's arrival at the shelter would not have coincided with the newspaper being on the floor; therefore, in the eyes of some, either flexi-time or the practice of allowing newspapers on to site could equally be cited as *the cause* of the workshop fire.

Of course, the reason that the inexperienced feel able to embark on such random selection processes is that the fire was comprised, as all accidents are, of a complex set of conditions (i.e. things, events and causes) that were each necessary for the effect in question. As a result, many believe, given that the absence of any one of the conditions would have prevented the fire, that they have found numerous root causes; that is, they believe that every one of those conditions has an equal right to be called a cause and that any one of them can therefore be arbitrarily singled out as *the cause*. However, that is not the way that it works (Hart & Honore 2002:45). Not all causes are causes as regards our central causal enquiries and not all events that follow one another are causally related (Hume 1739): note, Hume's *post hoc fallacy* reminds us that whilst 'B' following 'A' shows a coincidental relationship, it does not equate automatically to a causal one). Devoid of such realisation, the unwary, naive or inexperienced can cite a chain of causes that go back to the dawn of time itself.

Thankfully, commonsense recognises that the chain of antecedents can always be cut short and so, as regards the first point here,...

- Very often, we trace *the cause* <u>through</u> other causes (Hart & Honore 2002:43) (Fig.cec1a).

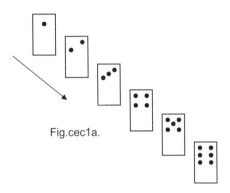

Fig.cec1a.

Recognising the Limit of Relevant Causes

Whilst it is possible to work downstream, we generally work upstream (Fig.cec1b); i.e. backwards in time from the rubble of domino 6. In so doing, we pass over an entire set of conditions (e.g. the newspaper on the floor, the presence of oxygen, the pallets leaning up against the work shop wall) that were necessary for the fire. However, we continue our upstream search because we are not interested in the cause of fire *per se*; we are interested in the cause of *this particular fire*. That is, we need to answer the question, "why was there a fire on this occasion when, normally, there would not be?" That question *is not* answered by listing the things (e.g. the newspaper and pallets) that, had they not been there, would have prevented the fire. Similarly, it is neither answered nor addressed by attempts to assign causative responsibility to those who are otherwise responsible for things like house-keeping or pallet storage policies; such things, normally addressed by those upstream, are amongst the matters to be considered for future prevention; they do not assist the central causal enquiry.

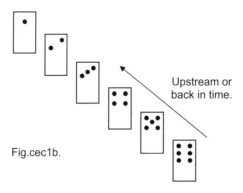

Upstream or back in time.

Fig.cec1b.

The critical requirement for the work shop fire was, of course, an ignition source. As it happened, we found that to have been introduced by a *deliberate act*. Whilst the discarding of the match was careless and the consequence not intended, we now have *the cause* and an explanation as to why there was a fire on this occasion when, normally, there would not be. Where the investigator is a finder of fact as opposed to one who adopts the role of judge, jury and executioner, the central causal enquiry (as opposed to the remedial one) usually ends at such a deliberate act. Indeed, the finding of *"a deliberate human act is most often a barrier"* (Hart & Honore 2002:44) that identifies the limit of the search for cause. Consequently, as regards the relevant point here...

- We do not trace cause *through* a deliberate act (Hart & Honore 2002:43); we can, but we need exceptionally good reason to do so.

Unfortunately, the problem that arises for users of models such as Bird's updated sequence and Reason's SCM (and other followers of Petersen of course) is that they have no effective operational definition (their default view of management as the cause of all accidents aside); i.e. they have no way of limiting the extent of their upstream search. Indeed, Reason (1990:189) believes that there *"are no clear-cut rules for restricting such retrospective searches"*; of course, that is a statement born of inexperience, confusion *and necessity.* Whilst we will look closer at Reason's SCM shortly below, it should be clear by now that both Petersen and Bird have, indeed, concocted a rule for restricting their searches; that is, ignore all unsafe or deliberate acts and move relentlessly on to management. However, and already noted, that then requires a wholly subjective decision regarding just exactly where to stop the theoretically unstoppable.

Before moving on, it should be obvious, having identified the cause at domino 3., that everything downstream becomes an explanation of the effect. That is, dominoes 4-6 provide an explanation of how the fire developed but, they have no explanatory force as regards *the cause* (Hart & Honore 2002:40-41); the downstream dominoes provide mere detail on the process of the effect. In addition, and whilst *the cause* was the discarded match, it should be obvious that there were other events (e.g. the smouldering and the wind) subsequent to *the cause* itself. However, and importantly, there are *always* events and conditions subsequent in time to *the cause* (Hart & Honore 2002:39).

Tail Chasing and Fire fighting –
The Effect of Relocating Cause Upstream

The proximate or root cause of the work shop fire was X's unsafe or deliberate act. In addition, we saw that everything downstream merely explained the effect; i.e. whilst dominoes 4-6 described the process or development of the fire, they did not assist an explanation of *the cause* itself. Consequently, it should be obvious that the practice of defaulting to assume that domino or Swiss cheese slice 1. (i.e. a management or organisational failure) will always be the proximate or root cause has serious side effects. When cause is arbitrarily relocated to the distal upstream point, everything downstream, including X's deliberate act, becomes lost in the general detail of the effect (Fig.cec2.). Sharp-end man and behaviour are essentially removed from the equation since the focus turns, ultimately and erroneously, to those things or occurrences that, had they not been there or occurred, might have prevented the fire or accident. However, attention to those things, regardless of how necessary, do not assist the central causal enquiry.

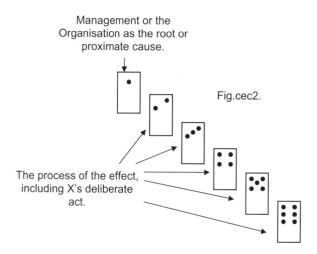

Management or the Organisation as the root or proximate cause.

Fig.cec2.

The process of the effect, including X's deliberate act.

Of course, it is not just 'sharp-end' man that gets removed from the equation. Responsibility for some of the numerous system components (or indicators in Tripod® (discussed later below) for instance) that are *invariably* associated with such accidents are often spread across several areas of the business. Consequently, attempts to transfer causative responsibility for the accident to the organisation require, and result in, numerous senior individuals being implicated by association; however, whilst each is put forward as *a cause*, none can be identified as *the cause*. In consequence, the organisation defaults to its relentless and forced obsession with the so-called system indicators; that is, it sets about the continual tidying up of conditions in the after-math of its accidents in the belief that these are *the cause* of *the cause* (i.e. they believe that conditions are the cause of the proximate cause and that these wholly negate downstream individual responsibility for deliberate acts).

Continuing on with that, we find the more critical problem perhaps. If domino or Swiss cheese slice one is indeed *the cause*, then any consideration of anything downstream becomes pointless since there is *nothing* downstream that can assist with any further explanation of *the cause* itself. Unfortunately, having moved through the deliberate act by way of associated conditions in an attempt to reach or 'justify' management as the cause, the only remedy is to then back-track through the conditions that led there in the first place in the belief that attending to these will attend to the alleged upstream cause.

Clearly, that is insanely circular and counter-productive; despite which, it is typical of far too many investigations and is a cause of the relentless tail-chasing and fire fighting that many organisations engage in (TYS). More importantly, individual behaviour at all levels of the business tends to go unaddressed. That said, responsibility for that behaviour is not always left unaddressed and is sometimes transferred arbitrarily to wholly uninvolved and innocent parties; with, as we shall see shortly below, occasionally devastating results.

Invariable and Unconditional Sequence

Numerous events and conditions are invariably involved in every accident. As Williams (2011) puts it, every man who ever got up for work and then travelled to work and was either killed or injured at work, *invariably* got up for work and travelled to work; later events aside, there is an invariable sequence in those accidents notwithstanding what has been said about cutting short the chain of antecedents. But, that invariable sequence *is not unconditional*; that is, just because a man gets up for work and travels to work does not mean that he is *bound* to be killed or injured at work. Nonetheless, according to Petersen (1971), Bird (1974), Reason (2004) and Manuele (2011) for instance (the latter's offerings coming via the American Society of Safety Engineers), every accident is caused, invariably and unconditionally, by organisational or management failures. However, commonsense (TYS), all of the data presented herein and, not least, experts in jurisprudence have categorically rejected any such notion; indeed...

*"This is in fact an absurdity both in practice and in principle. To meet such a standard there would have to be evidence that 'everything' (**all** other things, events, or states) apart from the set of conditions specified in the generalization was irrelevant, so that the specified conditions would be unconditionally and invariably sufficient. Neither in practice nor in principle is this possible. It would not be enough if those conditions not included in the generalization always in fact coexisted with those included, for then the specified conditions would merely be 'invariably' followed by the effect but not 'unconditionally'."* (Hart & Honore 2002:45).

Why So Many Dominoes and Slices of Cheese?

Before moving on, Bird's (1974) notion of cause raises some interesting questions. For instance, if the earlier referenced practice of Williams (2011) and the three domino depictions by Suchman (1961) and Heinrich & Lateiner (1969) are correct, why are there five dominoes in the Bird sequence? Indeed, if Difford's earlier noted alternative view of Heinrich's dominoes is correct then, logically, at least two dominoes in the Bird sequence are superfluous as regards any factually, knowable statement of cause. According to Difford (2004), if Bird genuinely believes that management are *always* the proximate or root cause then there is no reason for his sequence to look anything other than the depiction in Fig.ab1.

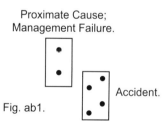

Fig. ab1.

As it is, Difford argues that the factors and labels that Bird attaches to his dominoes present nothing more than a checklist of conditions by which the unwary or untrained investigator unwittingly sets about confirming the premise. However, it should be clear by now that the only way that such a constant causative link to management can be made (i.e. an apparent confirmation of the premise) is if causes are persistently confused with something else. This would be an obvious problem for Reason's SCM (which effectively attempts to amalgamate Bird and Heinrich) but for a mechanism which clouds the fact that a persistent tracing of cause through a deliberate act is what is actually taking place (as we shall see below, it is the undeniably illogical notion of the latent condition via which Reason (2004) erroneously believes that this can be achieved and justified).

INTERIM SUMMARY

Petersen (1971), Bird (1974) and Reason (1997; 2004) have put forward models and theories on causation that are not only contrary to all empirical data but, also absurd in both practice and principle. Their causal over determination arises, not least, from ignorance (itself caused by naivety and inexperience) of the commonsense and logical need to cut short the chain of causal antecedents. Unaware, or in denial, of the critical distinction between transitive causes and incidental occurrences or conditions, their philosophies persistently ignore or dispute the only factually determinable root cause. In their relentless quest for cause beyond the barrier that is the deliberate act, they propose a standard of invariable and unconditional sequence that simply cannot be met. If their exceptionless belief that organisational or management failures cause all accidents was correct, accidents would be bound to happen upon their very existence; however, and as if it needed spelling out, that is not the case at all. Similarly, if Petersen etc were right then why, not least since Reason et al (2006) believe that organisational failures always exists, are the workplaces of the world not constantly piled high with dead bodies? If they are right that only management can cause an accident then only management can prevent one since, with no opportunity for sharp-end man to cause one, logic dictates that he cannot possibly have any opportunity to avert one either.

Thankfully, the nonsense of that is assisted firmly into bed when we understand and accept that the only logical assumption (if that is the right word) that can be made by the central causal enquiry is that...

- We trace *the cause* <u>through</u> other causes; but

- We do not trace cause *through* a deliberate act.

Chapter Six:
Reason's (1997) Swiss Cheese Model

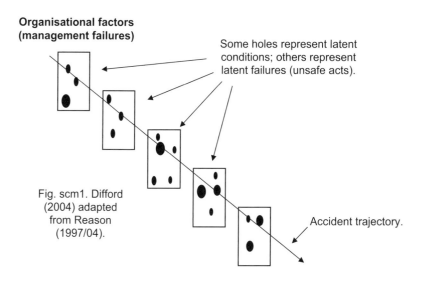

Organisational factors (management failures)

Some holes represent latent conditions; others represent latent failures (unsafe acts).

Fig. scm1. Difford (2004) adapted from Reason (1997/04).

Accident trajectory.

When something like multiple causation theory, Bird's updated sequence or Reason's Swiss cheese model (SCM) (Fig.scm1.) is presented for general consumption, that presentation includes an open and automatic invitation for others to 'pass a critical eye' over it. In particular, such critique will always be warranted and necessary where the model in question has been released on a 'suck it and see' basis. As such, critique is both a given and an expectation here since Reason (2004:236) offers that accident causation models such as the SCM "can only be judged" according to their effect on the system. However, and whilst that unscientifically places the cart before the horse, the task should not be left to others. As well as constantly evaluating and re-evaluating things (O'Brien et al 2004), authors should be continually seeking to disprove the theories upon which their models rest. Our world is "theory laden" and science moves forward by disproving them (Popper 2002). Since a theory can never be proved (i.e. no amount of corroboration proves a theory), only disproved, constantly relying on corroboration for it from within tightly-coupled or close-knit communities where nothing but corroboration is likely to emerge would, of course, be unscientific and obviously not what is needed.

The Essential Premise of the Swiss Cheese Model

Any evaluation or judgement of worth must have scientific method in mind if it is not to fall foul of, at least, subjectivity (Suchman 1967), vested interest (Stufflebeam & Shinkfield 2007), group-think or escalation of commitment. To get us going then, and for purposes here, the SCM premise can be stated as follows:

'The necessary condition for an organisational accident is the rare conjunction of a set of holes in successive defences' (Reason 1997: 2004: Reason et al 2006); a 'concatenation of multiple factors' (Reason et al 2006). All accidents are the result of 'latent weaknesses in the system' (Reason et al 2006) and errors are but 'consequences' of 'upstream systemic factors' (Reason 2000). Any catastrophic event arises from the adverse conjunction of several distinct casual chains (Reason 1990:188-9).

Normally, an analysis of the adequacy of the data presented in support of such a premise on accident causation should precede any consideration of the propriety of the premise itself (Froggatt & Smiley 1964:4). However, other than reliance and reference to the findings of certain high profile disaster enquiries worldwide (e.g. Challenger and the Herald of Free Enterprise), no data accompanies the SCM. Of course, enquiries such as those into the loss of the Herald do not have the same focus as needs to be maintained by the industrial accident investigator. With the greatest of respects, those enquiries are more akin to wide-ranging inspections and audits since numerous, causally unrelated, recommendations also emerge. As Justice Sheen made clear in the Herald enquiry, management failures that "were not causative of the casualty emerged in the evidence" (Report of Court 8074:15); such investigations therefore have a "second purpose" (8074:35). In any event, given the data in Chapter one above and the fact that the SCM premise is effectively a restatement of Bird (1974) and multiple causation theory, we have already seen enough to say that it is wrong and therefore disproved.

Reason's Initial and On-going Uncertainty in his Premise

Reason (2004:234) was asking whether 'the pendulum' had swung too far in management's direction well before the SCM was released. Indeed, given that the question, a critical reference to Hart & Honore (discussed shortly below) and other uncertain comments came at the end of his book, it appeared as though Professor Reason was doubtful of the SCM well before its release. Having stated that the "present situation [the organisational view] represents a significant improvement over knee-jerk 'human error' attributions", he adds that..

"some concerns need to be expressed about the theoretical and practical utility of this ever-spreading quest for contributing factors. We seem to have reached, or even exceeded, the point of diminishing returns, particularly when it comes to risk management" (Reason 2004:235).

Of course, and whilst the conclusion of that last statement had already been arrived at many years previously, it was wrong to imply that the improvements being spoken of had been made by way of attention to so-called contributing factors. Clearly, there was more than a hint of doubt in the worth or validity of the SCM and that doubt continues. Not least, the title of a relatively recent presentation by Reason that went by the name of *"Ueberlingen: Is Swiss cheese past its sell-by date?*" (Reason et al 2006) suggests an on-going uncertainty. However, if the question posed by that presentation is apt then, so too is this one...."by whom, when, where and how was Reason's Swiss cheese ever declared fit for human consumption?".

Reason et al (2006) accept that the Swiss cheese model of accident causation is not without its drawbacks and has not been accepted uncritically by the academic community. Young *et al* (2004:8) for instance feel that the "dogmatic insistence on identifying latent conditions could and should be challenged", especially where unsafe acts have clearly played a major role. Of course, Young *et al* would not have made that comment had they understood the true nature of the latent condition. That said, such criticisms should be listened to since remedial interventions based on methods with no scientific basis undoubtedly "do more damage than good" (Nemeth 2008:xvii). As it happens, the SCM has not been adopted or accepted by many outside of the academic community (TYS). Unfortunately, its underlying philosophy, with us since Petersen (1971) and Bird (1974), has been fully signed up to by the UK HSE, the majority of safety practitioners and many organisations. However, the validity of the philosophy becomes even more questionable in view of the following from Reason et al (2006:18)...

*"If we relax the requirement that every accident **must** involve the failure of one or more barriers, the inescapable conclusion is that we need accident analysis models that look equally to individual as to organisational influences. In other words, models of "human error" and organisational failures must be complemented by something that could be called socio-technical or systemic accident models".*

That statement, evidencing far more than needs to be discussed here, reveals much about the confusion that is the Swiss cheese model, its philosophy and premise or hypothesis. Firstly, Reason et al (2006) are clearly not in a position to deny the fact that an accident can occur without *any* so-called organisational 'barrier' having failed. Secondly, if 'they' feel that the requirement that "every accident *must* involve the failure of one or more barriers" can be arbitrarily relaxed then, the requirement was never valid in the first place. The requirement in question is crucial to the SCM premise. If it can be relaxed then its original specification cannot possibly have been based on any inherent belief in the hypothesis itself. In effect, Reason et al (2006) are confirming the invalidity of multiple causation theory and, the SCM premise itself.

Perpetuating the Management Failure Myth

Reason's (1997: 2004) Swiss cheese model (SCM) of accident causation (Fig. scm1) is a remarkably familiar one. Essentially, it is Bird's (1974) model with holes instead of spots and is equally confused and contradictory around certain topics. In keeping with Bird, and at first sight at least, it sees all accidents as resulting from a sequence of successive management failures. However, both Bird & Loftus (1976) and Reason et al (2006) deny that the respective models are linear or normative; which, according to Difford (2004), is purely academic since the result (i.e. relentless tail-chasing) is the same whether they are perpetually circular or never-endingly linear. Save for the SCM's extraordinary denial (indeed, contradiction and change of tack) that there is any such thing as a root cause (discussed shortly below), it mirrors all of the characteristics and erroneous assumptions of the earlier models of Weaver and Bird. Despite a belated attempt at concealment (Reason et al 2006), it is clearly another management failure model that ultimately ends up blaming a certain 'category' of person (albeit anonymously via the label of the so-called 'organisational accident' to which we will turn shortly below).

Whilst it appears to support it in places, the SCM firmly rejects the 'common cause hypothesis'. According to Reason (1990:174), unsafe acts are "usually caused by the unique conjunction of several necessary but singly insufficient factors" and the "same mixture of causes is unlikely to recur". Consequently, the SCM is firmly aligned to the idea that every accident has its own *"very individual pattern of cause and effect"* (Reason 2004:2). That said, it fully accepts that unsafe acts (error and violation) *"are the stuff of which accidents are made"* (Reason 1990: 2004:120) and that they are *"implicated in most organizational accidents"* (Reason 2004:17). However, the SCM completely side-steps the real issue in preference for the notion of the 'organisational accident' (Reason 2004:1) and the view that unsafe acts result from *latent conditions*; which, and not surprisingly since it mirrors the philosophy of the earlier models, are seen as stemming 'causatively' from successive higher level management failures. In fact, the SCM philosophy or bias is in such a state of denial and confusion regarding the real causes of accidents that it feels able to say this...

"Although fallibility is an inescapable part of the human condition, *it is now recognized that people working in complex systems make errors or violate procedures for reasons that go beyond the scope of individual psychology. These reasons are **latent conditions**"* (Reason 2004:10).

The italicised part of that statement, obviously, is not *"recognized"* here and it is difficult to see on what basis the man in the street (let alone a reasonable and objective investigator or analyst) might recognise it either. Save for academics citing one another, no support for it can be found and it is simply contrary to everything that we know from the field and Chapter one; including the findings of the court in the Sunday morning tragedy, HSE (2007) and common sense. Nonetheless, the statement allows the 'holes' representing unsafe acts (i.e. error and violation) to be relegated to secondary or incidental considerations...if they are considered at all (Fig. scm2). In any event, we shall shortly see how the true nature of the latent condition actually reduces the above statement to a circular absurdity.

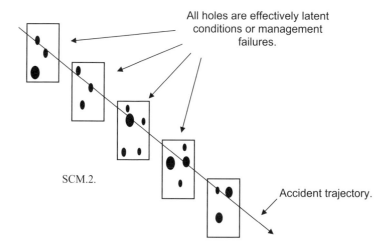

All holes are effectively latent conditions or management failures.

SCM.2.

Accident trajectory.

Essentially, perhaps of necessity, unsafe acts (especially violation) are subsumed into the model to such an extent that the need to confront them as a distinct and separate subject conveniently disappears. Even if they were to be considered separately the model would still default to blame the organisation since Reason (2000:120) feels that...

"virtually all" errors and violations have... "a causal history that extends back in time and up through the levels of the system".

Furthermore, the SCM and its supporters would have it that...

an unsafe act is "not a necessary condition" in most accidents (Reason 2004:17) since it is a "fact that no one failure, human or technical, is sufficient to cause an accident" (Reason et al 2006).

Whilst thoroughly confused, those statements, quite incredible to most no doubt, are contrary to everything that was (i.e. at the time the SCM was conceived of), and is, factually known. Not only is an 'unsafe act' a necessary component of an accident, it tends to be *the only* component (TYS). Even where a seemingly innocent lapse appears to be the immediate cause, "the necessary factor in the accident sequence is likely to be a violation" (HSE 1998:35). But, and like its predecessors, the SCM clouds reality by attributing the cause of a man's actions to a multitude of other factors. Indeed, effectively, the philosophy of the SCM and its supporters is such that we don't really need man (neither designer, manager or front-line worker for instance) in the equation at all; as the only causative agent, management (whatever that refers to) is omnipresent. However, and as was the case in the earlier discussion of free will, we find the SCM and its supporters to be putting forward philosophical hypotheses that experts (e.g. O'Connor 1995: Botham 2008) in that field have rejected. To suggest a requirement for an infinite number of causes of causings of an agent's own causal act "is not merely ridiculous on the face of it but also logically vicious" (O'Connor, 2002:61). Lowe's (2002) view on the matter has already been expressed insofar as it makes a man no freer than a boulder that rolls down a hill. However, analysis of O'Connor (1995 in part citing Chisholm) makes it clear that the only way that Reason and Reason *et al* could make such claims is by confusing the merely conditional with the sufficient causal; according to Chisholm, this confusion is one of the "most common errors" to which discussions of freedom and causation fall foul.

As regards *causes*, the SCM is so, apparently, convinced of its own philosophy that it clouds the requirement to validate findings. Indeed, whilst the earlier models produced streams of so-called 'root causes' that failed the system test, the SCM produces streams of so-called *latent conditions* that undergo *no* test at all.

Swiss Cheese Holes: Latent Conditions or Root Causes?

Noted earlier, Reason (2004) feels that the number of latent conditions identifiable by the SCM is limited only by the length of time that one is prepared to keep unearthing them. Indeed, devoid of any stop rules, Reason (2004:15) says that the SCM could trace the *"various causal chains"* back to the "big bang"; which, as it happens, is what most feel that they are doing when attempting to utilise the SCM or derivative Root Cause Analysis (RCA) software programs. In actual fact, users are generally under the (mistaken) impression that the SCM *is* identifying 'root causes' (TYS). Given the unrelenting reference to terms such as causal chains, workplace error provoking conditions and failed barriers and defences, users could be forgiven their impression since the model inescapably implies a direct causative link to management; i.e. a root cause by any other name. Indeed, when the first hint of the SCM model emerged (referred to at the time simply as "the diagram") it was stated that it was describing the *"dynamics of accident causation"* (Reason 1990/2003:208).

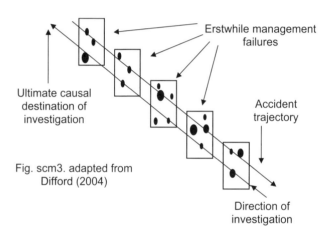

Fig. scm3. adapted from Difford (2004)

The diagram (see fig.scm3) showed the trajectory of an accident commencing with "failures at the managerial levels"; at that time, those failures were referred to as *latent failures* and would later undergo a change in title to *latent conditions* (of note, Reason (2004:236) offered that the term condition was "much more appropriate" *"in the causal sense"*). In concluding the relevant discussion, Reason (1990/2003:214) makes it perfectly clear that his latent failures (i.e. latent conditions) are the *"root causes"* of accidents. Despite which, following the report into the Ueberlingen air crash enquiry of 2002, Reason et al (2006:17) would offer that...

...a *'considerable strength'* of the SCM is that it *'avoids the notion of root causes'*.

Clearly, that is a remarkable contradiction if not an alarming change of tack. Whilst it should have encouraged certain factions of industry and the academic communities to have enquired into it quite deeply, it casts further and considerable doubt over the SCM premise in general. That said, certain writers and academics do appear to have their own particular views on cause. For instance, Dekker (2002:31) believes that "there is no such thing" as a "root cause"; indeed, Dekker would have it that there is "no such thing as *the* cause". As we know, and despite his view being wholly confused and contradictory, Hollnagel (2004) also considers the *notion* of a root cause to be 'fallacious' since he feels that, upon the finding of one, others can always be found (however, if 'another' root cause emerges, you obviously didn't find one in the first place...you must have identified something else). Reason also has an ill-informed opinion of the investigator's analytical skills. For him, a root cause is simply the 'contributory factor' that they happen to be working on when the time or money runs out (Reason et al 2006:9) (puzzlingly, he did not feel that to be the case with the Challenger disaster). However, ignoring the absurd and ill-informed nature of that, it highlights but two of the many problems that result from misguided approaches to causation.

First, there is an assumption that an SCM type root cause can always be found. However, we know from Hammer's study (HSE 1978), the field (TYS) and the findings of thousands of UK Courts under circumstances similar to the Sunday morning tragedy, that such a root cause *cannot* always be found; that is, a so-called organisational failure does not always exist (according to Difford (2004), causatively, it never does). Secondly, and more importantly, it highlights the tendency in many to view the so-called 'contributory factors' (which are actually components of the antecedent causal chain that invariably exist) as causes (something, incidentally, that HSG245 (HSE 2004d) also does). Where that tendency exists, users of the SCM and Events and Causal Factors Charts for instance invariably 'find' multiple root causes (often, they claim to find multiple immediate causes as well); indeed, BS8800 (BSI 2004) has also offered that "hazardous events generally have multiple causes", both immediate *and root* (see Appendix 3.). However, this is due to the misinterpretation and subsequent re-labelling of events and conditions in the antecedent causal chain (the so-called contributory factors). Of note, Williams (2011) offers that any investigator who claims to have identified multiple immediate, root and or systemic causes should be seriously taken to the task of logically explaining it by those who commissioned the report; according to him and Difford (2004), such an investigator is merely expressing (in a confused and elaborate way) his inability to identify *the cause*.

At first sight, the earlier comments from Hollnagel and Reason *et al* suggest a degree of naivety; this, since managers of the systems upon which they are proposing to act (systems which they claim to understand) need far more evidence than academic hunches can provide. Strangely, however, when alluding to the stop rules that might prevent the SCM search from going back to the dawn of time, Reason (2004:15) offers this;

Perhaps we should limit "the scope of analysis to those things over which the people involved – and most particularly the system managers – might reasonably be expected to exercise some control".

As it happens, and no doubt the systems driven reader will have noticed, this sort of rule would be well on the way to satisfying a key part of the test for a 'root cause'. But, and far from ever being able to identify and verify a root cause such that a manager might allow its finding to modify a system, the SCM now claims (if not finally concedes) that it doesn't identify root causes at all. Of course, it is actually pure necessity that compels the SCM to belatedly deny its 'notion' of the root cause in that respect. The accepted and scientific test demanded by the system rejects, as being clearly non-causative, factor after factor that SCM type searches churn out. In the same way, Reason *et al* (2006) are compelled to deny the relevance of logic diagrams since the tests applied to confirm or deny causal relationships there are also driven by logic and commonsense. Indeed, the tests that exist essentially equate to the master calculator that would show, irrefutably, that 17.42 + 33.31 does not equal 90!

Swiss Cheese Holes –
Latent Conditions or Mere Conditions?

Earlier, we noted Reason's (1990) inescapable conclusion that some of his terms are unacceptably vague and that his resident pathogen metaphor is far from being a workable theory; recall also that Reason's (1990:197-9; 2004:10) resident pathogens and latent conditions are one and the same thing. Consequently, Reason is fully aware that the notion of the latent condition is unacceptably vague and far from being workable. Whilst some (Wiegmann & Shappell 2003:48) see the fact that the SCM "forces investigators to address" latent conditions as being "particularly useful", many (Young et al 2004) have queried this where human error is an obvious and central theme. However, as will become obvious later below, neither set of authors would make their statements if they understood the true nature of the latent condition. Indeed, Wiegmann & Shappell's (2003) comment is slightly puzzling given their belief that the SCM does not assist analysis. In any event, the things that compel organisations (*not investigators*) to address the latent conditions that Wiegmann & Shappell are actually referring to are called audits and inspections.

Contrary to the belief of Hollnagel (2004:55) for instance (recalling that Hollnagel co-authored the Reason et al (2006) document), Reason's (2004) introduction of the term latent condition was not the heralding of a new and important concept; it was confirmation of a flaw that was otherwise concealed by terminology and academic verbosity. The SCM purports to be an accident causation model and the implications for it should have been obvious from the passage by Hart & Honore that Reason (2004:236) cited...

"causes are what made the difference, mere conditions, on the other hand, are just those [things] that are present alike both in the case where accidents occur and in the normal case where they do not; and it is this consideration that leads us to reject them as the cause of the

accident, even though it is true that without them the accident would not have occurred...to cite factors that were present both in the case of the disaster and in the normal functioning would explain nothing: such factors do not 'make the difference'...". (Hart & Honore 1985 as per 2002:34)

Whilst Reason (2004:236) offered that his latent conditions were "not quite" of the same "character" as Hart & Honore's, it is clear from discussions above and elsewhere (e.g. Reason 2004: Reason et al 2006) that the mere condition is fully incorporated into the latent condition (indeed, already noted, its only other component is error or violation). According to Difford (2004), discussions on what a latent condition (the holes) is or might be are misleading since the problem relates to what they claim to be able to do; nonetheless, it will not hurt to touch lightly upon them here.

As regards the variation in the size of the holes depicted by the model, these can have no real relevance since a mere condition is a mere condition regardless of whether it is the size of a pea or the size of Saturn (or, regardless of whether it is the size of a hose or the size of an iceberg perhaps). Similarly, as regards the size of the holes insofar as they represent unsafe acts, these could only vary in relation to their effect or outcome. In the main, those potential outcomes will already have been identified by risk assessment and/or similar or more scientific tools; very likely, in well defended domains, they will also have been graded according to approved risk matrices. Consequently, any assertion that the holes are merely alternatives to spots on dominoes is already far from fanciful.

As regards Reason's (1997: 2004:9) description of the holes being in a constant state of 'flux', this can only be due to the fact that they are *unsafe acts and conditions* created and removed by people as opposed to the system (acts etc mostly created and removed unbeknown to the organisation since they tend to exist for relatively short periods of time and are usually not present during audits for instance). The SCM cannot describe the holes as being static otherwise it would be compelled to identify them (notwithstanding of course that they become miraculously static after the event). However, models such as the SCM (including any so-called 'versions' or derivatives of it) have no predictive capability since they support, not least, multiple causation and the notion that all accidents are unique. In that respects, any model or explanation that they put forward for an accident will be misleading (if not pointless) since the basis is a flawed notion of cause. Consequently, they communicate a flawed message, not least remedial intervention wise, since the only way that an accident could or might happen according to their philosophy is contrary to reality.

Whilst here, and in reality, the TYS found that the vast majority of accidents involved but a single act that occurred, more often than not, during properly determined periods of self-supervision. That said, and whilst a violation does not have to involve an error (Reason 1990:195), the 'single act' often involved the "lethal" combination (HSE 1998:49) of both a violation and an error. In most cases, the system of work would have been tolerant of the error; but, the circumstances created by the violation knowingly placed the individual/s outside of the protection that was otherwise afforded by the system (for instance, if a man working at height slips, his fall is arrested by his harness; but, if he opts not to wear or attach the harness then the foreseeable and manageable slip becomes a fall). Consequently, there is a behavioural boundary that has safety on one side and, chance on the other (Patterson 1950:68); noting, importantly, that chance often plays a part in determining the outcome of safe behaviour as well (HSE 1998:44).

Where an 'unsafe condition' existed (recalling that these result, nonetheless, from 'unsafe acts') it was only in 12-14% of cases that it was created by someone other than the individual or group that was ultimately affected. Where a man was injured or killed due to no fault of his own, the TYS found that an unsafe act or omission to act by a front-line colleague was predominantly the root or proximate cause. In many instances, the short-lived duration of the condition created by the unsafe act was unavoidable (but not always) by the injured party/deceased and undetectable by routine inspection and monitoring processes; i.e. it was not created by the system, it was created contrary to the system by a man beyond the 'control' of the system. As with certain conditions, violations tend to be visibly obvious for very short periods; i.e. they are there one minute, and gone the next. As such, they are typically outside of the system's control. Of course, employees committing knowingly wrongful acts generally try to conceal them from management (TYS); something, incidentally, that would be unnecessary if management authorised or condoned them.

If the holes in the cheese were system driven they would be readily and immediately detectable by audits and/or inspections since internal systems managers are constantly monitoring for evidence of non-conformance. Even if such holes were capable of going undetected by the managers responsible for the relevant system (or, indeed, were even undetected 'holes' in quality assurance and safety plans) they would undoubtedly be detected by external auditors; that, of course, is the very reason for utilising them; they inform the business of non-conformances (potential and actual) and improvement opportunities.

The holes cannot be *latent* in the proper sense of the word either since they would, by their very nature, be undetectable (of course, these should be detectable by the SCM in diagnostic mode since such holes in the cheese cannot possibly be there one minute and then gone the next...unless, that is, the SCM only works retrospectively). That said, internal system managers and external auditors are constantly looking for evidence of substandard products or practices; not least, they are looking for evidence that such might enter or leave the business. When such non-conformances *are* detected or suspected, the system demands a process whereby the root cause of the problem might be identified and considered (ISO 9001:2008: BS 8800:2004). Reflecting back on our earlier root cause discussion then, the organisation and its external auditors therefore specify a requirement for an internationally recognised process that a). the SCM denies is possible; and b). would not be able to assist with even if it did not. Indeed, even Dekker, a stalwart of the 'blunt-end' school, concedes that as regards engineering design implications at least, the SCM has no systems approach or diagnostic capability at all (Stoop & Dekker 2009). Of course, where an investigation identifies a potential system improvement opportunity, the SCM type philosophy blocks an analytical question that is vital for prevention; i.e. can this accident or non-conformance re-occur once the proposed remedy has been installed? In the absence of such a question (or, in the presence of a less than certain response), cause must be assumed to be still in place and, at best, a workplace inspection has been conducted...not an investigation and analysis.

Accident Causation Model or Workplace Inspection Checklist?

According to Reason (1990: 2003:198-9), his resident pathogen metaphor...

> "...shares a number of features with the now largely discredited accident proneness theory, though it operates at a systemic rather than at an individual level [and] would suffer a similar fate if it were found that pathogens could only be identified retrospectively in relation to a specific set of accident circumstances...to have any value it is necessary to establish an a priori set of indicators relating to system morbidity and then to demonstrate clear causal connections between these indicators and accident liability...".

Before continuing, it should be noted that Reason has only ever provided retrospective comparisons (Difford 2004); however, it is the assumed causative relevance of those comparisons that creates problems. Whilst the above statement appears to be saying that a set of indicators exist or have been found that identify a clear and persistent causative link to accidents, it *does not* say that. What it refers to is indicators of *accident liability* and that, quite simply, is not even remotely the same thing and is not what is required at all. Despite which, it is indicators of accident liability that comprise the labels that Reason (1990/2003:200) actually attaches to his slices of Swiss cheese.

Reason (1990/2003:203) goes on...

"A basic premise of this framework is that system accidents have their primary origins in fallible decisions made by designers and high-level (corporate or plant) managerial decision makers".

Clear from the opening statement above, Reason was fully aware that the SCM defaulted to transfer blame upstream; this, to such an obvious extent that he likens the result to accident proneness for organisations or senior managers. However, Difford's (2004) analysis shows that it works *only* at an individual level (i.e. not at a systemic level as claimed) and we will turn shortly below to see how and why he can say this. Nonetheless, by way of the second statement, it is clear that such blame can only be transferred if a clear causal connection exists from an accident to a high-level decision maker. Indeed, the basic assumption or premise is that **all** *system accidents* must be shown to have such a causal connection or the SCM fails and is disproved.

Quite bizarrely, albeit in keeping with numerous contradictions that Difford (2004) has found in Reason's work, Reason (1990/2003:205) goes on to say that *"it would be naive to assume that the pathology or otherwise of a given line department is purely a function of higher-level decision making"* (the UK parliament for one also agrees (see s.36), individual errors or violations do not default to become either the system's or the organisation's). Furthermore, Reason (1990/2003:205) says that line managers could *"cause good decisions to have bad effects"*. Consequently, we find Reason disproving his theory himself insofar as the required causal link to senior management cannot, by his own admission, always be made. Indeed, and leaving aside the fact that the SCM's causal statement is an invariable and unconditional impossibility, many might wonder why he ever released it in the first place.

Undeterred, Reason (1990/ 2003:200) presented a number of 'indicators' (all reliant on the basic flawed premise nonetheless) and it will assist other matters to explore these briefly here. For ease of immediate purposes, the 'indicators' can be taken as the General Failure Types (GFTs) forming the basis of Shell's Tripod-Delta®

initiative (see table tscm1). Reason was involved with Tripod's development and it had the role of human error in accidents as its original focus (Hudson et al 1994). According to Reason (2004:237), *"identifying and eliminating latent conditions proactively still offer the best routes to improving system fitness"* and it is by way of GFTs or similar that he sees that as being achieved. Not surprisingly, and in keeping with Bird's (1974) earlier discussed 'list', all of the failure types are focussed on negative aspects such as ergonomically *poor* design, *poor* quality of hardware, *ineffective* communication and so on. Consequently, in its 'revised form' as a tool to assist safety checks or audits, the 1996 version of Tripod was based on the 'principle' that the best way to control human error is via attention to the working environment (Cambon et al 2006). Whilst the epidemiological triad is clearly incorporated into the process, the GFTs (hence, and very problematically, the 100s of so-called indicators) actually fall under a heading of *latent failures*; i.e. latent conditions or resident pathogens.

Latent Failures			
Hardware	Design	Error enforcing conditions	Housekeeping
Maintenance management	Procedures	Incompatible goals	Communication
Organisation	Training	Defences	
Readers who are unfamiliar with Tripod type tools should note that indicators accompany each of the GFTs and that these typically number in excess of 200.			
Table tscm1. Adapted from Reason (2004).			

Whilst there is nothing wrong with the GFTs as the basis of an aid to audits or inspections perhaps, serious problems arise for users who are under the impression that those *types* of headings will assist them with the investigation and causal analysis of an accident (TYS; also see Appendix 1). Using the SCM in an attempt to show a 'causative' link from the general failure types to accidents tends to result in users feeling as though they are constantly revisiting the same aspects of their systems (TYS). In fact, most reported that they simply could not see the causative relevance in the numerous factors that they were forced to visit (primarily, of course, because no such causative link exists). Unfortunately, none of those spoken to during the TYS were aware that they were predominantly looking at mere conditions; all believed that they were identifying (and hence remedying) root causes. The same is true for those who attempt to utilise RCA software that have GFTs or similar for 'guidance' (TYS). Indeed, Reason (1990; 2003:152) discusses Tripod-Beta and says this...

"Tripod-Beta [designed to be compatible with Tripod-Delta] is a PC based tool...for conducting an incident analysis in parallel with an event investigation. Interaction between these two activities provides the investigators with guidance as to the relevance of their fact-gathering and also highlights avenues of investigation leading to the identification of contributing latent conditions – General Failure Types in Tripod parlance."

Before moving on, it should be clear that investigators are being forced down an erroneous and biased route. Note also that Reason, having said that latent conditions are root causes, now feels that there is such a thing as contributing root causes.

Whilst the indicators (the labels attached to the Swiss cheese slices) put forward by Reason (1990/2003:200) in support of his premise (noting, extremely importantly, that his premise relates to accident causation, not accident liability) are not exactly the same as the GFTs, they are of the same genre. Consequently, it will not hurt to look to the GFTs to see how they relate to the SCM or its premise.

Tripod was developed by teams from the Universities of Manchester and Leiden (Hudson et al 1994:58) following reviews of various case studies and reports. Logically, the information available to them should only have related to the stated 'unsafe acts' in the reports and the conditions that existed at the relevant times. Of course, the term latent failure or latent condition should not have been found within any of the historical reports insofar as it was not available until Reason and/or those teams invented it. However, whilst discussing Tripod-Delta and its original conception in general, Reason (2004:134) says that the GFTs were "identified in part from the recurrent latent conditions associated with past events". Obviously, that was not possible. Consequently, it is fair to say that a term was devised and then retrospectively applied to historic data; that is, analysis must have been influenced by the philosophy underpinning the newly invented term and confirmation bias was likely running amok. But, if either the philosophy or reality of the term was not fully understood or wrong, then so too would have been the analysis of the data and the resulting remedial advice.

Reason (2004:134) went on to say that "GFTs, in turn, create the conditions that promote or exacerbate unsafe acts"; however, that presents an absurd circularity that will become obvious shortly, if it isn't already; for now, if the GFTs are neither conditions nor unsafe acts, what on earth are they? Finally, he says that "after observing operations in a number of operating companies and studying their accident records, 11 GFTs were chosen as best reflecting those workplace and organizational factors most likely to contribute to unsafe acts" and create lost time injuries. However, and is if things weren't becoming a little uncertain and hazy, Hudson et al (1994:58) offer that latent failures are "potential causes of future accidents". In addition, they introduce the term "triggering events" and offer that accidents cannot happen unless 'unsafe acts' interact with them (worse still, they also believe that accidents have multiple immediate causes). They then say that when "the combination circumvents available defenses, the result may be an accident or a near-miss". Alluding to the latent failures as proximate or root causes, they say that these are "often present long before" the accident occurs.

Whilst Tripod is not under the spotlight here, the reason that its GFTs are generally problematic for causal enquiries (TYS) is probably obvious. That aside, the reason we paused here was to see if they provided anything of substance for the SCM premise; clearly, they do not. Reason needed to demonstrate "clear causal connections" from senior management to all accidents. Terms like "contribute to unsafe acts", "chosen as best reflecting", "most likely to contribute", "promote or exacerbate", "contributing latent conditions", "may cause an accident" and "potential cause" are simply too vague. Whilst some might be content with the likes of the GFTs as so-called indicators of accident liability, they are, at best, nothing more than workplace inspection headings. All the same, they constitute the essence of the labels attached to the SCM's slices of cheese; indeed, effectively, they are a restatement of the labels attached to Bird's (1974) dominoes.

In concluding here then, and improvement opportunities aside (noting, *extremely importantly*, that these too must undergo the same rigorous system tests that root causes are subject to), what tends to be generated by the SCM is a limitless stream of so-called 'organisational failures' that purport to be linked causatively to the subject of the enquiry. Indeed, organisations 'aligned' (often unknowingly) to the SCM and similar philosophies are constantly repeating the same 'remedial' cycle for every accident. Nonetheless, the cycle of accidents continues as does the 'disbelief' in their occurrence amidst systems that were presumed able to prevent them; disbelief, no doubt, that befell NASA in March 2011 (re a contractor's fatal fall from height) and the owner of the Deepwater Horizon in April 2010. However, and already offered, the accident investigation process should not be reduced to some sort of glorified workplace inspection; especially if the findings might be misinterpreted as root causes. Unfortunately, that is exactly what the SCM tends to do; but, no-one has told the companies that use either it or the so-called Root Cause Analysis programs that have its philosophy running amok in the background. Consequently, it is not just certain 'investigators' but many organisations that are unwittingly doing little more than conduct audits and inspections in the aftermath of their accidents.

'Blame the System...Save the Day'

In a document revisiting the SCM (now described on the 'tin' as an accident model), Reason et al (2006) offered that there were a number of 'versions' of the SCM and that a number of uses can be made of them. However, and whilst neither the author nor the TYS found any effective difference whatsoever in these so-called versions, such academic juggling is neither expected nor required. The SCM is either an accident causation model...or it isn't; constantly changing the label on the tin does not alter what you've got inside it. Nonetheless, with the deckchairs rearranged, the Titanic sailed on.

Whilst man is part of the equation, accidents will be possible on each and every occasion that the task or process involved is executed (Firenze 1971: 1973). Even though Firenze was an early member of the multiple factors and epidemiological school, he conceded that the realistic probability of the system eliminating man failures was 'zero'. Despite which, the relentless pursuit of the conditional continues in the belief that this will in some way alleviate the problem.

When serious or disastrous outcomes result, the knee-jerk reaction today is the same as it was in Heinrich's time and beyond. Following the enquiry into the loss of the Titanic for instance (a collision involving one of the biggest mere conditions imaginable), the first recommendation was *more legislation* (Senate Report 1912). If the reader finds that document on-line they will see that, whilst essential for the preservation of safety and life at sea, the recommendations did not address *the cause* of the collision; at best, the recommendations might reduce the severity of outcome of a similar accident but, not the likelihood of the accident's recurrence. As we know, ships continue today to collide with objects and other ships despite the on-board existence of the most advanced systems available to support them; the essential common factor is, of course, man. Whilst he is at the helm of any activity, the system is at his mercy.

Reference to the massive and tragic loss of life resulting from the capsize of the Herald of Free Enterprise in 1987 might further assist here. Firstly, Reason (2004:12) feels that a 'latent condition' involved with this tragedy was the "capsize-prone design" of the vessel (recall from the earlier discussion regarding the Parliamentary Office of Science and Technology that Reason (1990:256) originally said that the "top heavy design" of the vessel was a "latent failure" that made it "inherently unsafe"). However, nowhere in the final report on that casualty was any such suggestion made (nor was it possible) and it may be taken as *read* that the Herald was no more capsize prone than a self-righting life boat is. It is well known (not least by those who sail them) that a roll-on-roll-off ferry can, depending on the action at the helm, capsize quickly if sufficient water has been caused to enter its car decks (van Gorp 2005). However, the design of the Herald does not cause or compel water to enter its car decks during its normal functioning (it cannot opt to flood itself). Man has to act or omit to act in order for that to happen and the problems arise when improvement opportunities are confused with causes. Nonetheless, Reason's claim shows the extent to which the SCM will go in its drive towards upstream factors, the 'blunt-end' and beyond. But, why would an investigator who is primarily searching for cause even mention such a thing...is the organisation being asked to consider changing all of its ships because, under certain abnormal circumstances, they will capsize? In such instances, the real question for the investigator is not so much "what have you identified" but, "why have you identified it?" Perhaps the SCM would recommend the melting of all icebergs in order to stop ships colliding with them (which, of course, would then leave them free simply to collide with rocks and/or one another).

Numerous findings and recommendations emerged from the enquiry into the loss of the Herald (despite which, and extremely tragically, the M/S Estonian went down). For many, the one-year suspension of the Herald Captain's 'license' (Report of Court No. 8074) might have been key. But, such a suspension would only be beneficial if it provided something positive prevention wise. Certainly, in the short term at least, that suspension had the same effect that a temporary disqualification from driving might have; but, if there is no attempt to improve or modify driving behaviour in the future, what is the point beyond any notion of short-term punishment?

The notion of the disaster as an organisational accident (Reason 2004; Young et al 2004:4) also does nothing to assist things. It is short-sighted and incredibly damaging; not least, it is contrary to the view of the applicable law as evidenced by the failed prosecution against the company (*R* v *P&O*). According to Difford (TYS interim), the case might not be certain under the UK's Corporate Manslaughter Legislation (CMCH: 2007 Act) either. He asks whether the Captain's actions, in light of his autonomy, instructions and responsibilities, might place the ship's owners beyond the 2007 Act's 'management failure test'; this, since the organisation will not be liable on the basis of any "immediate operational negligence...or indeed for the unpredictable, maverick acts of its employees" (CM 6497:12). He also argues that the 2007 Act could commence the driving of a wedge between certain levels of the business since, in defending 'itself', the organisation automatically presents a named and identifiable individual as being responsible (noting that Gross Negligence Manslaughter as it applies to individuals is alive and kicking).

Whether Difford is correct or not, there is a clear wake up call, not least, for the UK safety profession insofar as Parliament has again acknowledged the fact that an appropriately specified system does not prevent accidents; indeed, and quite bizarrely given their relentless stance on the subject, Reason *et al* (2006:16) fully agree! However, the system cannot be modified to reduce an organisation's accident problem whilst the same old 'holes' receive nothing more than the same old 'fixes' (Bignell & Joyce 1984). Where causation has to be proved (e.g. in Corporate Manslaughter and Gross Negligence Manslaughter cases) the law recognises that an individual's behaviour can break the chain of causation; i.e. an accident can be the sole fault of the employee (*Ginty* v *Belmont*). Indeed, laws exist in most jurisdictions to ensure that individuals can be held accountable for causing industrial accidents. These laws or provisions would not be necessary or available if 'management' caused all accidents (see for example s.7. & 36. HSWA). Furthermore, dissenters would need to prove (by becoming fully embroiled in a discussion on causation for instance) the likes of Hume and Hart & Honore wrong. That said, blame is not involved here and so *Ginty's* reference to 'sole fault' could be misleading. The Courts (e.g. *Smith* v *Baveystock*) have consistently refused to accept the sort of absurdities that would result from SCM type philosophies and this is based more on "fairness and commonsense" than notions of blame or fault (*ICI* citing Fleming). In any event, let's return to the Herald of Free Enterprise.

With the focus of attention now turned more or less exclusively towards its owners and managers, the Captain appealed the suspension of his license. Whilst it is not suggested to be the case here, this has been found to be a typical reaction where other parties have encouraged the relevant individual to believe that responsibility lies elsewhere (TYS); indeed, attributing the cause of our behaviour to the situational is the psychological starting point for most of us (Jones & Nisbett 1972) (also see *ICI* v *Shatwell*) as general psychologists such as Professor Reason know all too well. However, and in the instant case here, it may have overlooked the fact that the Court had found "serious negligence" on the Captain's part to have contributed to the loss. In fact, the Court (Report No. 8074:12) had stated that the Captain, having taken the ship to sea with the bow doors fully open, "*must accept personal responsibility for the loss of his ship*".

The appeal (*Re The Herald*) considered that such a statement would reflect "the initial reaction of any seaman…indeed any layman". The Captain, however, submitted that the system of checking that class of ship's seaworthiness was adopted by all of his fellow Masters. Therefore, in assessing "the standard of conduct to be expected of the reasonably prudent cross-channel ferry Master", it was against these that he should be judged. The appeal Court accepted that "general practice is usually cogent evidence of the standard of reasonable care". But, it was "unhappy about designating a practice of failing" to ensure that bow doors were closed to be a system. The need to make proper checks before sailing was "*so obvious that it was folly to ignore it*". As such, dismissing the appeal and refusing an early return of his license, the Court decided that adopting the practices of other Masters did not evidence the standard of reasonable care, it evidenced "*general and culpable complacency*" (*Re The Herald*)". That said, we, here, must remain conscious of the terrible burden that he carries.

Whilst there were many things that conspired against the Captain that day to defeat behaviour that normally resulted in success, the point here is not to do with the Herald. The point here is that the tendency in many to view an *individual's* accident as being an organisational accident can have far reaching, negative and counter-productive implications. Not least, it can lead to apathy and a sort of blinding as regards individual responsibility (wherever it lies) for the consequences of certain acts and omissions. Indeed, more than a few individuals spoken to during the TYS had confided that, whilst they themselves felt that the accident in question was their fault, others had convinced them otherwise. Similarly, the TYS found many Directors and Senior Managers who were aware, or coming to realise, that they relied on the notion of the organisational accident as a sort of shield or excuse...as an easy opt out. Indeed, one stated that "...we have become happy to blame it on the system and put our suits away until the next hearing or funeral". But, why do so many do this?

Failed Barriers and the Organisational Accident – Fact or Fiction?

The essential, if not *the*, premise of the SCM is that *"the necessary condition for an organisational accident is the rare conjunction of a set of holes in successive defences"* (Reason 1997;2004:11); clearly, organisational accidents and failed barriers are inextricably linked and so we may need to hop from topic to topic in these final sections.

First of all, the premise is out of step with everything presented earlier to dispute Petersen's (1971) multiple causation theory and Bird's (1974) updated sequence (noting, of course, that the entire book is challenging all such models jointly and simultaneously). In addition, enough of that evidence was available to Reason at the time of the SCM's development; not least, Heinrich's theory (which remains valid) should have been seen as standing in direct contradiction to it. Secondly, we saw earlier above that safety (hence an accident) has not been found to be dependent on the organisation, regulatory compliance or any formal system at all. What's more, in addition to finding no supporting empirical data here either, the TYS has not found accidents to be dependent on the failure of any barrier or established practice of work; accidents occur irrespective of the status of the system and any so-called barriers.

As part of the TYS, three organisations (one engineering, one construction and one house builder) were kept under active observation for periods of 6 months, 4 months and 30 months respectively. Those three organisations (plus seven others that were analysed retrospectively) were important owing to one common factor; none of them had anything in place that came remotely close to satisfying the basic expectations of risk or quality management systems. However, all that needs to be said here is that (of the primary three) their safety performance was not affected despite vast variation in risk profile, size and turnover. Indeed, even Reason (1990:208) is forced to concede that "*very few unsafe acts result in actual damage or injury, even in relatively unprotected systems*". In addition, and whilst it is not a measure as such, they all suffered far fewer reportable accidents or process failures than the organisations with whom they interacted and might reasonably be compared (Fig.nfb2).

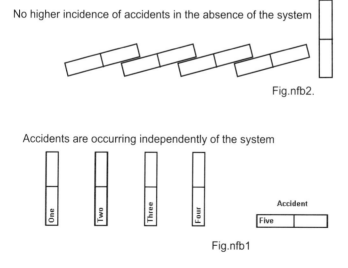

No higher incidence of accidents in the absence of the system

Fig.nfb2.

Accidents are occurring independently of the system

One Two Three Four

Accident

Five

Fig.nfb1

Nonetheless, according to the organisational school, and in work at least, people do not have accidents. The SCM and its supporters feel that accidents are caused by the successive failure of barriers, defenses, safe-guards or controls (words used interchangeably here) and that people just get 'innocently' caught up in them. In addition, man himself is considered to be part of the defensive mechanism. But, the SCM makes a critical distinction insofar as Reason (2004:6) feels that "the one sure fact about an accident is that defences must have been breached or bypassed" (emphasis here being needed on the word by-passed). Furthermore, and equally critically, Reason (2004:11) notes that "active failures [error and violation] are committed by those at the *human-system interface*..."; i.e. those at the sharp-end.

Since any discussion regarding the nature or functions of barriers will only cloud matters, it is enough for purposes here to say that barriers can either be physical or managerial. That said, we should be wary of the SCM notion of a barrier since anything that is inevitably waiting to fail cannot possibly be a barrier. Similarly, a physical barrier cannot be effective one moment and then ineffective the next. To consider otherwise would be to attribute consciousness and decision-making capability to the otherwise lifeless and inert. The brakes on your car cannot 'choose' or 'decide' to fail. Consequently, the notion of man as a barrier is a fatal misconception. Something that can opt or decide not to function as intended cannot possibly be a barrier. The alternative is to consider a system wherein one barrier is knowingly (and uncontrollably) capable of damaging another!

As regards man existing at the 'interface' of the system, Reason is correct. However, elaboration is required. An interface is a boundary or a border and, as such, we must view man as existing independently or outside of the system even though he acts upon and/or within it. The driver of an earthmover does not become part of that machine or system any more than a pilot becomes part of a plane or a train driver part of a train. In their garages, automobiles are beautifully finished, inoffensive ornaments (Heinrich 1941:25); however, on the road, they become deadly weapons (Porterfield 1960). No man who is required to conform to an expected practice or specified system of work becomes part of that system. Therefore, he must be initially identified, considered and accepted as being a risk to it. Whilst he may well be viewed as an entrusted custodian of faith and expectation, he cannot be viewed as a barrier; not least, since he is prone to random and intermittent failure. In that respects, given that the vast majority of managerial (if not all) controls require the cooperation of the human element, Reason's (2004:7) view that the multiplicity of defences are "mutually supporting" is, whilst underspecified, not entirely wrong. In reality, however, neither these nor the so-called defences-in-depth (tragic realities of certain military strategies (Luttwak 1976) as it happens) can be assumed to provide proof against human failures; not where man has been involved and, not where man will be involved.

By virtue of its belief in man as a barrier, the SCM incorporates a barrier into the equation that is not a barrier at all. Consequently, supervision aside, it becomes clear that the only way that many of the organisation's so-called barriers can be viewed as "mutually supporting" is by way of the fact that they are totally dependent...on man. Any notion of mutuality must, therefore, emphasise that men are generally *entrusted* to perform their work safely. Of course, man means *all men*. As such, Reason makes the same unwarranted distinction between sharp-end man and so-called blunt-end man as HSG48 was accused of earlier above. No man is part of the system, irrespective of his position in the organisational hierarchy. Consequently, to blame one man when another man fails is absurd. The transference of blame from one man to another in the way sought by the SCM is a luxury afforded only to the criminal and civil courts; however, unlike the SCM, each has strict rules where causation is concerned. In any event, the industrial accident investigator is not primarily concerned with legal causation, he is primarily concerned with commonsense causation since effective remedial intervention arises only from this.

The view that an organisation's barriers result from compliance with legal and system requirements must also be handled with caution. The organisation can only control the controllable (recall the Judge's view in the Sunday morning tragedy). Since we are here considering the proposition that man is outside of the system, we are also compelled to consider that the organisational barriers end where man's interaction begins. If so, man becomes the critically active component and it is difficult to see (when all other barriers are satisfying the system and legal requirements) how the blunt-end (which is, of course, simply someone else's sharp-end) can have exposed the sharp end to unnecessary risk; indeed, when things are viewed this way, logically, it is clear that it is the sharp end that is, in fact, unnecessarily exposing the organisation (we will return to the matter of barriers shortly). So, given that it is obviously wrong, why is there a default focus of attention post-accident on the system rather than the man; where has the notion of multiple barrier failures and organisational accidents come from?

Organisational Accidents – Products of an Ill-founded 'Stop-rule'

According to Reason (2004:1), *"Organizational accidents have multiple causes involving many people operating at different levels"* of the business. By contrast, he says that *"individual accidents are ones in which a specific person or group is often both the agent and the victim of the accident"*. In an end note, which is worth reproducing in 'full' here, Reason says that *"Individual accidents can, and usually do have organizational origins. Indeed, as...Shell Expro has pointed out, an offshore fatality is typically the result of a chain of at least seven distinct failures. Although it is not always easy to draw hard and fast lines between individual and organizational accidents, this book [i.e. Reason's book] argues that it is useful to treat them as distinct kinds of event"*.

I will deal with this section in two parts. Firstly, regarding the claim that an offshore fatality "typically" requires "at least seven distinct failures", that is nonsensical. Given what is factually known (recall fig.nma1. reproduced below) about 'accidents', Shell Expro believes that any accident that it suffers, including any near-miss or even a man stumbling over his own shoe laces, typically requires at least seven barriers to fail before it can occur. That, quite simply, is wrong.

Accident: **Injury:**

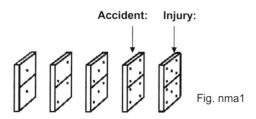

Fig. nma1

The accident or near-miss accident sequence involves only dominos 1-4. An injury or loss producing accident sequence involves all 5 dominos. Note here then that the *accident* and the *injury* are two distinct occurrences; one is the result of the other. Often, it is a matter of chance as to whether injury or loss results; indeed, chance often has a large part to play in severity as well.

Initially, one might be inclined to offer the benefit of the doubt and assume, at least, that it wasn't the same seven barriers failing on every occasion. However, that actually makes things worse since the alternative is particularly bleak; i.e. risk management must be in such a state of disarray that, regardless of the remedial interventions put in place following a fatality, seven totally different safe-guards are knowingly going to fail and cause the next death (or accident, or incident or instance of environmental pollution...the label is irrelevant). But, if it is genuinely that predictable in advance, how can it so predictably occur...is the organisation helpless or is it being taken on a wild goose chase? Perhaps, recalling the discussion just a few sections above, the so-called causes are 'predictable' only in *retrospect*! For certain, the method of 'analysis' being used (whether Tripod or SCM derived) is not resulting in any future predictive, preventive capability (already noted, the SCM's defence to that is that the next accident will be different). Perhaps the following might assist Shell Expro to understand in part why they feel able to say that 'at least' seven distinct failures will typically occur;

"As always in such analyses, there is the problem of defining the explanatory time frame. Any catastrophic event arises from the adverse conjunction of several distinct casual chains [note that Shell Expro contradict that]. *If these are traced backwards in time, we encounter a combinatorial explosion of possible root causes, where the elimination*

159

of any one could have thwarted the accident sequence. There are no clear-cut rules for restricting such retrospective searches" (Reason 1990:188-9).

Alternatively, Shell Expro might wonder why a failure on something that is so wholly reliant on soundly established principles of science and engineering is analysed by way of the metaphysical.

Of course, the apparent problem of defining the explanatory time frame is actually the fault of the SCM, not its users. Contrary to Reason, and as we know, *there are* clear-cut rules for restricting such searches; the problem is, they do not suit the SCM...indeed, they defeat it. Unfortunately, the SCM philosophy is shared, usually unwittingly (TYS), by far too many (BP's Deepwater Horizon report (available on-line) being a classic example). Consequently, the result of an SCM type search is an *'embarras de choix'* of mammoth proportions. The nonsense that is Reason's "combinatorial explosion" of possible root causes arises from a fundamental error that the earlier example of the work shop fire was designed to highlight and off-set. The SCM problem is further compounded by the fact that it forces users to mistake dozens (or any number of options from the hundreds available) of the so-called accident liability indicators for 'possible root causes'. However, a properly trained investigator disposes of such non-causal factors or conditions in a heart-beat.

In reality of course, the SCM does not allow the search for 'causative' factors to end at 'seven'. Already noted (Reason 2004), the process can continue back until the dawn of time; i.e. it has no operational definition and, hence, no logical termination point beyond the subjective choice of the 'investigator'. In theory, seeing how some such as Hollnagel (2004) feel that "analysis can always be taken one or more steps further back", the dawn of time is not really a barrier to an SCM type of search at all. Indeed, and having already noted his view that there is no such thing as *the cause* let alone a root cause, Dekker (2002:183) believes that "there is technically no such thing as the beginning of a mishap". I do not understand what is meant by a mishap (I for one would not describe, for instance, the Los Rodeos airport or Uberlingen tragedies as such) but our family dog, as a puppy, once had a mishap on our living room carpet. If I accept that there was no start to that, then there is no end to this sort of mishap.

Organisational Accident or Individual Accident?

As regards the generality of Reason's (2004) statement at the start of this section, it is clear that the notion of the organisational accident is purely an academic one. Furthermore, logical analysis of it confirms that it is simply not possible for *any* accident to occur that does not have *a person* (i.e. human error or behaviour) underlying it. Whilst a little surprising, even Petersen (1979:15) conceded what he described as a "painfully obvious and simple truth", "people, not things, cause accidents" (of course, the acknowledgement becomes even more profound once you accept that management or the organisation, as a non-entity, is also *a thing*). Indeed, over a fourteen year period (the 2nd TYS having commenced), the TYS has yet to disprove Difford's (1998) contention that human behaviour (suitably defined and 'acts of God aside') will be at the root of any accident. Of course, and more importantly in some respects, the SCM is also unable to deny Heinrich's theory or his finding that unsafe acts caused 88% of accidents insofar as that was the figure he put forward in relation to them. Indeed, some might feel that the SCM is so completely reliant on Heinrich that an absence of formal acknowledgement and reference to him in Reason's work is unusual.

By virtue of Reasons' comment regarding it not being *"always easy to draw hard and fast lines between individual and organizational accidents"* one might have assumed that, in the majority of cases, such lines *were easy* to draw; i.e. there must be numerous factually worked examples showing clear distinctions between organisational accidents and individual ones. However, no examples are provided. Indeed, all of the 'examples' provided in Reason's (1990) and (1997:2004) works are retrospective comparisons between the findings of like minded (as regards the extent and type of trawl) high profile enquiries and the SCM philosophy. As a result, and similar to the absence of any causal detail from the UK HSE on the 30% (at least) of deaths that were not organisationally driven according to the Courts, clear cut statements regarding just exactly how the system is being by-passed and what *the cause* was is absent. The Ueberlingen document (Reason et al 2006) is a classic example of what results from an SCM analysis (referred to there by the way as the Reason Model Framework). Essentially, it appears as an inspection/audit report since it touches on numerous incidental areas that should not be of any concern to an investigator who is objectively seeking, *and verifying*, cause.

Absence of reference to specifics is problematic, not least, since Reason (2004:194) says that his book is not concerned with the "traditional health and safety measures" that are directed mainly at "*individual* work accidents"...he says that his book's "focus" is on the "limitation of organizational accidents". As such, one might assume that the causes of organisational accidents are different to the causes of individual accidents; however, such an assumption would be wrong. Reason (2004:232) says that "*both individual and organizational accidents have their roots in upstream organizational and managerial factors* [and both] *have their roots in common systemic processes*". In addition, he says that "*both types of event are due to latent conditions*". Clearly then, at this stage, there is absolutely no logical difference between an organisational accident and an individual one and latent conditions *are* root causes according to the SCM; or, to put it another and more familiar way, management failures are the ***root causes*** of ***all*** accidents.

Whilst the latent condition is an undeniable statement of cause, Reason (2004:11) says that the critical distinction between an active failure and a latent condition relates to the "*location within the organization of their human instigators*". In addition, Reason (1990:188) says that a latent failure "*is an error or violation that was committed at least one to two days before the start of the actual emergency and played a necessary (though not sufficient) role in causing the disaster.*" Consequently, given what is known about things that exist regardless of whether an accident occurs or not (and ignoring the ridiculousness of Reason's arbitrarily selected one to two day requirement), Reason's SCM relies on the existence of mere conditions (Tripod indicators for instance) that might in some way be non-causatively associated with the accident. However, since the SCM defaults (by way, according to Difford (2004), of an 'insanely circular mechanism') to see all accidents as being caused by management, there will always be events and conditions subsequent in time to the cause (Hart & Honore 2002:39). As a result, according to Reason's SCM, there is no such thing as an individual accident; they are all, invariably and unconditionally, organisational ones. Consequently, and whilst our 'legal' discussions are not concerned with civil or criminal liability *per se*, only the way that the legal mind approaches cause, Reason's SCM equates to strict liability; indeed, writers such as Petersen, Bird and Reason are compelled to reject the potential (let alone reality of) for any type of intervening or superseding cause.

Clearly, Reason's latent condition is in no way similar to Hart & Honore's 'mere condition' and Reason's (2004:236) reference to it was something that was rightly questioned. Indeed, Difford (2004) does not understand why Reason ignored the fact that Hart & Honore were actually providing an additional hammer for the numerous nails already in place around the lid of the SCM's coffin. Alternatively, there should have been some sort of attempt (notwithstanding that Reason's 1997 & 2004 works should have been devoted to such) at a discussion on causation; however, and not surprisingly perhaps given the impossibility of the task, Reason (2004:231) says that his book *"is not the place to get embroiled in the philosophy of causation"*.

Latent Conditions: Legally Absurd – Philosophically Ridiculous

Reason's latent condition (constructed of causal language) defaults to blame an upstream individual and is therefore aligned to his (2004:230) so-called *"person model"*. In defining how such causal responsibility is determined from a legal viewpoint, Reason (2004:232) quite correctly relies on the following from two eminent Professors whom he, and Courts around the world, recognise as experts in the field of causation;

The causal explanation of the accident is brought to a stop when it is explained by a deliberate act in the sense that none of the antecedents of the deliberate act will count as the cause of the accident. A deliberate human act is most often a barrier and a goal in tracing back causes...it is often something through which we do not trace the cause of a later event and something to which we do trace the cause through intervening causes of other kinds. In these respects a human action which is not voluntary is on a par with other abnormal occurrences: sometimes but not always we trace causes through them, and sometimes but not always we trace effects to them through other causes (Hart & Honore 2002:42/44).

Whilst the essence of that statement might not be obvious at first sight, it can be taken as an accurate general expression of legal, logical and common-sense views of how cause is located and identified in the context here. However, it **must** be read and applied in accordance with the following...

In distinguishing between a cause and a condition, two contrasts are of **prime importance**. *These are the contrasts between what is normal and what is abnormal in relation to a given thing or subject-matter and between a free deliberate human act and all other conditions. The notions in these contrasts lie at the heart of most metaphors that cluster around notions of cause and* **must** *be used in any literal discussion of* **the facts which they obscure**. (Hart & Honore 2002:33).

Whilst Reason (2004:236) is fully aware of the basic contrasts between causes and conditions (notably, he cites them under a somewhat understated heading entitled *"Some Problems with Latent Conditions"*), the absolute requirement that they be applied to the metaphor at the heart of his SCM has clearly been avoided. Consequently, the facts that such avoidance obscures *remain* obscured and one result is the apparent causal over-determination (as some might put it) which leads organisations like Shell Expro to make the sort of claim cited earlier above. However, Shell Expro's investigators, and hundreds of thousands of others around the world, would not make such claims if they understood the true make-up of the latent condition.

By way of a re-cap of the points made during the work shop fire and other discussions above, we know, in the context here, that...

- Causal relationships are not always transitive (of note here, and whilst SCM supporters should not be able to agree with it, Reason *et al* (2006:16) concede that any other conclusion would be *"logically invalid"*!).

- The chain of causal antecedents is logically cut short.

- Very often, we trace *the cause through* other causes to reach a deliberate act.

- We do not trace the central causal enquiry *through* a deliberate act.

- There are *always* events and conditions subsequent in time to *the cause*.

- Everything downstream of *the cause* (the deliberate act) is but a further explanation of the process of the effect.

- The SCM standard of invariable and unconditional sequence cannot be met.

To the above points, we might add the following from Hart & Honore (2002:45)...

- The view that cause can be selected or singled out from a complex set of previously identified conditions that are known to invariably produce the effect is "misleading".

- It "radically misrepresents" the character of actual situations both in and outside the courts where we ask and succeed in obtaining satisfactory answers about cause.

In order to explain the causally, counter-productive effect of the resident pathogen or latent condition, we will re-visit the earlier example of the work shop fire to see how that becomes an organisational accident according to the SCM. First of all, some additional information regarding that fire (also see Figslc1. below);

Domino 1:
X's parents meet by accident in 1952.

Domino 2:
X is born.

Domino 3:
On the morning in question, X' gets up.

Domino 4:
X goes through his normal routine and goes to work. Today, he decides to go by bus rather than use his car.

Domino 5:
X's colleague discards a newspaper onto the floor even though an empty waste bin is visible some 40 feet away. X steps on the paper several times. X lights a cigarette and discards a lit match directly onto the floor and leaves soon after. X is seen smoking outside of the permitted zone behind the smoking shelter. He says he was sheltering from the wind.

Domino 6:
A rat is seen to drag the lightly smouldering newspaper under a nearby fence.

Domino 7:
The smouldering newspaper is carried by the wind to some wooden pallets outside of the work shop. The pallets ignite and fire spreads to the work shop.

Domino 8:
Fire detectors activate and an automated call goes out to the fire brigade.

Domino 9:
A fire engine attends and extinguishes the fire but the building is a total loss.

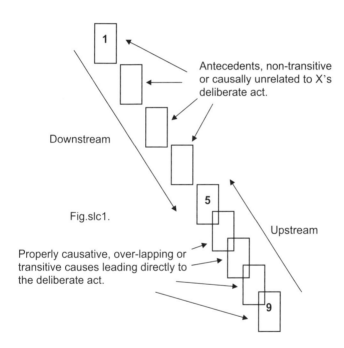

Antecedents, non-transitive or causally unrelated to X's deliberate act.

Downstream

Fig.slc1.

Upstream

Properly causative, over-lapping or transitive causes leading directly to the deliberate act.

Whilst we would not consider events 1-4 to be in any way relevant, they remind us about how and why we work through certain causes to reach *the cause* or *deliberate act*. At event 5., the causal explanation is exhausted since none of the antecedents of the deliberate act shown by events 1-4 will count as *the cause* of the fire. Everything upstream of event 5. is superfluous irrelevance as regards *the cause*, and everything downstream is but an explanation of the effect. However, provide the same information to an SCM disciple and, apart from finding the accident to be an organisational one in which no single individual was to blame, the following would not be unusual...

SCM 1:
The site wide fire risk assessment has not considered this eventuality. If it had, the fire would not have occurred.

SCM 2:
No proper policy on pest control exists. If it did, the paper would not have been able to leave the smoking area in the way that it did and the fire would not have occurred.

SCM 3:
The safety culture on the site is poor otherwise X's colleague would not have thrown the newspaper onto the floor and X would not have ignored it; similarly, X would not have discarded matches onto the floor. If the safety culture on site was good, the fire would not have occurred.

SCM 4:
There is a policy relating to the purchasing of pallets as well as instruction on how many should be stacked on top of one another. However, there is no clear policy prohibiting the stacking of pallets against walls. If a proper policy had existed, the fire would not have occurred.

SCM 5:
There is no policy in relation to the treatment of wooden pallets with fire retardant. If a policy had existed, the fire would not have occurred since tests confirm that the paper would have burned away before it could have ignited the pallets.

SCM 6:
The wind on the day was northerly and this produces a draft in the smoking shelter. No record exists of any consideration having been given to the positioning of the shelter and it is not, therefore, in the ideal position. If X had not been forced to leave the shelter he would

probably have noticed the smouldering paper and/or the rat. Proper positioning of the shelter would probably have prevented the fire.

SCM 7:

Management control is poor. Smokers are often seen outside of the permitted area with lighted cigarettes. If management enforced its rules then X would have remained in the smoking area and probably noticed the smouldering paper and/or the rat. Enforcement of smoking rules would probably have prevented the fire.

SCM 8:

Reminding smokers to be more careful is not enough, habits are hard to break and we all make mistakes. If the organisation is a caring one then smokers should be encouraged, and assisted, towards quitting.

At first sight, the above appears to be a thorough investigation. However, the view that SCM type 'investigations' are more akin to workplace audits or inspections is clearly borne out in that numerous causally unrelated improvement opportunities have been identified. The reason that they appear to be causally relevant is due to the investigator having listed things that, had they not been present, might have prevented the fire. But, the question as to what has caused the fire *is not* answered by listing things that would have *prevented it*. In addition, such lists, causation wise, can only be made in ignorance of conditions. Whilst the fire might not have occurred had the regulatory breaches or short-falls represented by SCM 1.-7. not been present, they are, nonetheless, also present when *no* fire occurs. As such, they are not causes and the problem for the SCM is that it is neither logical, justifiable nor supportable to force the central causal enquiry relentlessly upstream through them.

Clearly, the SCM needed to surmount that problem (notwithstanding that the problem is, in fact, logically insurmountable) and it believed that it had done so by way of the absurdity that the latent condition reveals itself to be. The SCM philosophy, wholly flawed, is that the existence of a mere condition, in place for at least 1-2 days by way of an upstream individual's error or violation, is enough to transfer causative responsibility away from the so-called sharp-end and into the abyss of the so-called blunt-end; i.e. it seeks to transfer blame from one individual to another by way of the merely conditional. Worse still, it unwittingly conceals this by way of its ridiculous belief that there exists both individual accidents and organisational ones. However, it should be blatantly obvious by now that there is no such thing as an organisational accident; they are all, and can only be, individual ones.

Aggregation – Another Flaw in the Concept of the Organisational Accident

One of the criteria for an organisational accident is *'job title'*. Furthermore, we know that the SCM defaults there by way of a flawed mechanism. 'Sharp-end man' is factored out of the equation and, in a stroke, both cause and responsibility are arbitrarily transferred to *persons* upstream in the organisational hierarchy; i.e. to the blunt-end or, more correctly, to someone else's sharp-end since all men, regardless of title, work at the *interface*. However, Reason (2004:231) sails past another insurmountable problem for the SCM in that the 'organisational accident' in the immediate context here is contrary to the criminal law in England and similarly aligned jurisdictions. The label of the organisational accident can only be applied when the errors or violations of several senior managers (i.e. multiple latent conditions) are grouped together or 'aggregated' such that their combined faults become the organisation's. Unfortunately, once again for the SCM, that *is not* possible.

Reason (1990 & 2004) references the Herald of Free Enterprise in a number of places and so that case can be utilised here to highlight yet another aspect of the SCM that had already been rejected by experts. According to Justice Sheen (Report of Court No. 8074:14)...

"All concerned in management, from the members of the Board of Directors down to the junior superintendents, were guilty of fault in that all must be regarded as sharing responsibility for the failure of

management. From top to bottom the body corporate was infected with the disease of sloppiness".

That statement continues this day to circulate the health & safety communities and is highly attractive to supporters of the SCM type philosophy. However, in the context here, it is a highly misleading and emotive inaccuracy. Aggregation has been "summarily rejected" by the UK courts and the Law Commission's view was that it would be "unsatisfactory" to extend such a doctrine into the relevant legislation (Law Comm No. 237:96). Consequently, we find yet another aspect of the SCM that experts in the relevant field have already rejected. That said, even if an organisation *could* be a cause, attending to the downstream processes is akin to constantly applying bandages to continually recurring wounds without ever stopping to consider the cause of the wounds themselves.

Knee-jerk Organisational Error Attributions

Contrary to Reason's (2004) belief that the organisational accident is a "significant improvement over knee-jerk 'human error' attributions", it is, in fact, a knee-jerk reaction in the opposite direction that is both seriously flawed and highly questionable. Indeed, depending on the loss involved, it is nothing short of appalling. The label of the 'organisational accident' has had devastating consequences for innocents caught up in its seemingly anonymous yet all encompassing nature. HR professionals, directors and those involved with governance for instance have reported having been made to feel personally responsible for the outcome in question (TYS). Directors and senior managers of construction and engineering companies for instance have been similarly tarred and affected. Wholly devoid of solutions, some academics have taken to referring to those workers who knowingly gamble and loose as being heroes. However, I do not view the actions of men who, sometimes in open and defiant displays of bravado akin to Russian roulette, reap the ultimate outcome that they always knew was possible.

Without risk takers, much of industry would grind to a halt since the excessively risk averse would not set foot on a construction site, let alone climb a ladder or descend into a compressed air face. I myself am a calculated taker of very high risks; my clients premises are risk-laden and in my private life I still ride high powered motorcycles and SCUBA dive regularly, with a single bottle of air, to depths well in excess of 100 ft. I do not expect the known risks to materialise; yet, I buy lottery tickets in the belief that odds of millions to 1. against me *will* materialise. Some men, for whatever reason (and only they know) create and/or assume risks that are neither created nor assumed by the process and they do so in the belief that the known risks will not materialise; *yet*, they too buy lottery tickets.

I do not view as heroes those whose gambles take the lives of their colleagues or members of the public and I certainly do not see the after-math and heartbreak that many leave behind as being in anyway the result of heroism. Such appeals to emotion are utterly disgraceful.

Apart from the many other problems that the term causes, the notion of the organisational accident can attach a particularly unpleasant and unnecessary label. Despite Reason's earlier noted attempts to off-set it, the SCM *is* playing the management blame game and, according to Difford (2004), is the only reason that its philosophy is attractive to some; not least, the UK's Health & Safety Executive. However, the notion of the organisational accident and the term management blurs the fact that management is comprised of people. Those people, many of whom have worked their way up through the ranks and have lives to lead and families to take care of, do not expect to go home on a day so randomly selected by chance with the label of aggregated killer attached to them. Similarly, they did not attend work on the fateful day with any level of disregard for human life, quite the contrary (2nd TYS); in fact, most were once at the so-called sharp-end themselves.

All that can be said to assist any that have been so burdened is that the degree of preventability has never been determined (Heinrich 1941:18; 1959: 1980: TYS). Consequently, failures arising within adaptive and compliant organisations in this new millennium must be viewed as improvement opportunities. However, for the system to improve, it must first be reliably informed. Unfortunately, the improvement opportunities that exist are confused and distorted by academic notions of organisational accidents and of businesses as tightly coupled 'complex sociotechnical' entities with some sort of 'psychopathology'. Such views, sometimes appearing to be driven by an absence of hands-on or practical understanding, are out of step with both reality and system management requirements (requirements, incidentally, that are not affected by academic notions of complexity; either you understand the reality of the organisation and its operational and system requirements...or you don't).

As it is, the sign-posts to the required intervention strategies are often discredited, assisted by appeals to emotion, on the basis that they are an inappropriate consideration for a 'caring employer'. However, the cycle of accidents continues and some are now realising that the label of 'caring employer' sits rather uncomfortably alongside the reality of negligent service provision.

A Fatally Confused School

In reality, such notions are driven by a remedial arsenal of such limited scope that the only recommendation forthcoming is to continually address the same aspects of the system. The organisational school have resisted any other approach in the mistaken (if not preferred) belief that investigations are halted when violation is discovered. They profess that the only remedy that can result is one whereby the individual involved is blamed and told to be more careful. However, and whilst that is a million miles away from the truth, the following might highlight the brick wall that certain academic communities have come up against.

As part of a number of large scale studies into driver violation and error, Parker, Reason, Manstead and Stradling (1995) offered this...

"...a new approach to accident prevention is required, focussing on reducing violations by persuading drivers not to drive in a dangerous manner" (HSE 1998:34).

Apparently, outside of the factory gates, certain academic communities are happy to 'blame' the driver and do little more than seek ways to *'persuade'* him to be more careful (apparently, the normal view of the situational always being causatively responsible seems capable of an arbitrary about turn). However, if that same driver violates whilst on the road for his employer, certain academic positions change completely to one where the violation can only have been caused by someone else; miraculously, a remedy presents itself but, on closer inspection, it looks incredibly familiar. For instance, an in-depth study for the Department for Transport (Clarke et al 2005:38) found that "work-related accidents are not fundamentally different in their causal structure to any another road accidents"; the errors and violations of high mileage drivers "did not appear markedly different from those of the general driving population". However, the following was the best that could be offered in the relevant conclusion...

"The solution here may involve driver training, but consideration must also be given to altering organisational and work structures that may be shaping these drivers attitudes and behaviours."

That is a difficult statement to understand given that there is absolutely nothing whatsoever (indeed, their evidence is to the contrary) upon which to even remotely base the belief that the organisation might be shaping behaviours, let alone attitudes. Once again, the naivety of the academic rears its head insofar as there is a belief that systems managers might set about arbitrarily interfering with 'organisational and work structures' devoid of any evidence that there is anything wrong with them. The notion that training might form part of the solution is also dangerous; if the causes of the behaviours are unknown, how can any training possibly be devised?

Organisational Accidents and Barriers –
Myths born of Misrepresentation

For many, accident investigations are conducted in order to prevent recurrence, not to apportion blame. However, both parts of the statement are conveniently misleading and false. As regards blame, for all but the most naive, this is often an inevitable by-product and no more will be said on that here. As for prevention, that is a strong word; especially where the wit or whim of man is involved. Furthermore, why is the investigator supposedly able to find something that will prevent a recurrence when the original risk assessor, clearly, was not? Given that an SCM search defaults to by-pass human error and anonymously (or so it would seem) re-label it as an organisational accident, it will only identify matters that have already been previously addressed. Consequently, there is no more point in an SCM analysis than there is in the UK HSE's advise to 'review the risk assessment'. In addition, the fact that the SCM school sees all accidents as being different (Reason 1990:174) means that prevention is effectively impossible. Given, not least, that the original risk assessment will essentially always be capable of being viewed as inadequate, the organisation will always be at fault. However, this cannot possibly be correct. So, returning to our earlier posed question but from an alternative perspective, why do many automatically default to the organisation or system when an accident happens? Why is it not the person's accident? Why is it someone else's accident?

Those questions have no notions of blame in them and so there must be no notions of blame in your answers. Your answers must be factually based, objective and logical. So, consider the three diagrams below and the additional question posed there. Before answering, go for a walk or have a cup of tea. Perhaps you might take a tour around your workplace to think about things (taking care not to expose yourself to unnecessary risk whilst preoccupied since I would hate for either myself or my great, great grandmother to be cited as the proximate cause of your accident).

When an accident happens (and for immediate purposes), let's say that we initially have the state of affairs depicted in Fig.ah1.

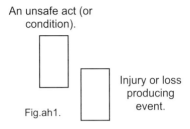

An unsafe act (or condition).

Injury or loss producing event.

Fig.ah1.

However, analysis of empirical data over the past 80 years shows, consistently, that the underlying cause of any preventable accident is human behaviour; which, alters fig.ah1. to that as depicted at Figah2.

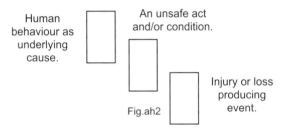

Human behaviour as underlying cause.

An unsafe act and/or condition.

Injury or loss producing event.

Fig.ah2

So, the additional question that you should ask yourself and then go away and objectively ponder for a while is this..."Why do so many default to a mental image of the accident as depicted in fig.ah3. below when the problem needing attention is as depicted by fig.ah2 above?".

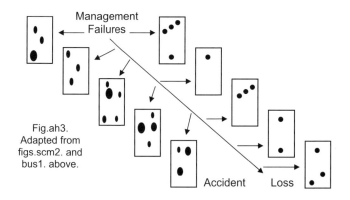

Fig.ah3.
Adapted from
figs.scm2. and
bus1. above.

Management
Failures

Accident   Loss

Many have a mental image of an accident that will be similar to one of those depicted in fig.ah3.; i.e. a Bird or SCM type model. Furthermore, they genuinely believe it to be a true and accurate representation. However, it should now be clear that they have, in fact, been unwittingly and erroneously programmed to both view and investigate industrial accidents in that way. Petersen (1971) aside, the cause of the initial problem was Bird's (1974) re-labelling of the first domino in his updated sequence. With management at the fore there became no way for an accident to occur other than by way of a loss of management control; i.e. by way of failed barriers. The SCM has followed this lead and is the same...the accident cannot happen unless multiple barriers or controls fail. The only difference in the SCM depiction and Bird's dominoes is that one sees things toppling whilst the other sees things as going through (but, the result is the same). Consequently, the scene is set by way of a mental image of *'things management'* having to fail or fall before an accident can happen. When we install the confusion that is multiple causation, the misapplication of epidemiology and the notion of the latent condition into the equation, the rest, as they say, is history. Consequently, large factions of industry and the academic community have been lead unwittingly up the garden path with occasionally devastating results (TYS). Indeed, even editors (e.g HSW 2011:1) are blissfully unaware that their SCM utterances are, in fact, specious.

Contrary to the main premise of the SCM and the general view of Reason et al (2006) (i.e. Reason, Hollnagel and Paries), the majority of accidents, let alone all, are neither caused nor bound to happen due to an absence or flaw in such barriers. That said, the academic view is incredibly confused. For instance, Hollnagel (2004:68) has said that an "accident can be described as one or more barriers that have failed, even though the failure of a barrier only rarely is a cause". He goes on to say that once the cause has been identified, "barriers can be used to prevent" future similar accidents (Hollnagel 2004:69). However, and noting that such is clearly supporting the common cause hypothesis, just exactly how prevention is going to be achieved when he has said that the failure of a barrier is rarely a cause is a mystery. In addition, it is practically impossible to understand given that Hollnagel is a firm supporter of the SCM and, by default, Reason's (1990:174) earlier stated belief that the "same mixture of causes is unlikely to recur".

Had a 'serious' accident been suffered by either of the primary three organisations discussed earlier above, it would undoubtedly have been attributed to multiple management failures and regulatory breaches (i.e. to latent weaknesses or failed barriers and defences). However, the TYS applied multiple accident scenarios to all of the organisations involved and in no case would a regulatory breach or system non-conformance have been *the cause*. A barrier simply cannot be effective system wise one minute, then, for no apparent reason, be ineffective the next. The only logical conclusion is that something other than the system is causing the accident in the same way that something other than the system was largely responsible for safety in its apparent absence. However, the essential question that is raised and left unanswered by Dekker (2002:34) for instance is what, then, is responsible for safety when no accident arises seeing how the latent weaknesses etc were always in existence?

The starting point for many will require a clear and unambiguous acknowledgement that, acts of God aside, human behaviour (suitably defined) causatively underlies all accidents. Not least, such acknowledgement requires a unanimous recognition of a second inescapable fact, violation is capable of defeating any system.

Unfortunately, human error and behaviour is confused with ergonomics (a term that now includes the even wider notion of human factors) which associates safe behaviour with the design of places and things (Chapanis 1991). However, ergonomics over-looks the fact that the benefits from the vast array of safety features, controls and adjustment options provided in modern workplaces and/or as part of a safe system of work tend to rely on user 'discretion'; that is, individual decisions (*free will*) are central to system success and, by default therefore, central to system failure (Bignell & Joyce 1984). Consequently, until error and behaviour is addressed as a distinct, necessary and separate subject, the situational and management blame cycle will continue to roll on.

"It is highly likely that the majority of accidents could be avoided if individuals followed the safety procedures laid down for their protection. However, some other, as yet concealed and overriding, influence appears to modify behaviour so as to reduce the level of safety accepted. If this is under the jurisdiction of the individual, it may be accepted voluntarily. The motivations for this are unclear as yet, but may prove to be the most important element in accident causation" (HSE 2004c:1).

For me, that is one of the most profound statements ever to have been passed to the UK Health & Safety Executive. Whilst my work in the field amidst the TYS would challenge its belief that the motivations (and, hence, the remedies) for such behaviour are unclear, the reader should consider the entire statement carefully since it drives a juggernaut through much that all too many currently hold so dear.

INTERIM SUMMARY

Essentially, Reason's numerous assumptions are restatements of those that were made in error by Petersen and Bird with an additional emphasis, and incredibly heavy reliance, on the denial of free-will. Of course, when the SCM was conceived of, there was too much *academic* debate surrounding free-will in general for it to have formed any part of either a model or a theory. That said, we have seen enough, not least in relation to agent causation, to reject the no free-will school's argument for purposes here. Indeed, the weakly camouflaged and occasionally appallingly worded appeals to emotion via which certain academics and writers attempt to convince employers that they alone, invariably and unconditionally, are the sole cause of a man's behaviour, are preposterous. The arbitrary way in which blame (and let's be perfectly clear, it is nothing but an expression of blame) is so casually, and without exception, transferred to others is morally reprehensible; it is also fatally counter-productive. If no worker has the opportunity to exercise free-will then upon what do they base the belief that such a statement is false given nothing but job title? Whilst we wait for an answer to that, we might recall that the very people upon whose behalf, and without any authority whatsoever, they make such claims have, in fact, themselves rejected the very notion. Given that the common man's view of the causes of his own behaviour are contrary to the academic notion and, that the common man's view is supported by giants such as Chisholm, O'Connor and Botham, the no-free-will argument reveals itself to be nothing more than a convenient myth...a complete fallacy. The only reply to that can be that man does not know his own mind; however, you must reduce him to an automaton, to a mindless moron, before you can even remotely consider entertaining that.

As it is, the no-free-will school effectively reduce men to zombies; how they manage to get up for work, let alone cross roads, is beyond me. They argue that management, machinery and the environment combine, without exception, to cause the behaviour of men at work. That said, they do not explain how these multitude of sensory inputs are now able to compel a man who, previously, had no decision making capability whatsoever. Similarly, they do not explain how, upon leaving work at the end of the day, his free-will (responsibility for his behaviour) miraculously returns; that said, it must surely return sporadically during the day since, absent the ability to answer the call of nature, the result would be a combinatorial explosion of neverending mishaps. Of course, man himself disagrees with all of this and *that* is enough for us. In any event, the multiple factors that exist according to the misapplication of epidemiology in the work place are representative solely of conditions...not causes. The misapplication of epidemiology itself is attributable, for purposes here, to ignorance (if not denial) of the critical distinctions that exist, and *must* therefore be drawn, between causes and conditions; supported, furthermore, by a preference for the metaphysically absurd and ridiculous over the only way that cause can be traced in practice and in principle according to time honoured logic and commonsense.

As regards their general assumptions, there was enough information available to Petersen and Bird for them to refute their own claims; consequently, there was even more available to Reason. Nonetheless, he persisted in the face of numerous (far more than have been identified here) absolute indications that his belief was wrong. In fact, there is only one thing right with the SCM. Of course, what is wrong with it stems initially from the fact that when you base something on the general designs of others without realising what their flaws are, you naturally incorporate their flaws into your own design.

Effectively, the SCM's slices of cheese and essential labels are a variation on Bird's (1974) theme. Of course, the SCM's only principally factual statement relates to that which had already been made by Heinrich's theory; yet, there is no recognition of that. As it happens, Heinrich's finding, as modified, that unsafe acts cause all accidents is as close to being correct as the SCM gets. However, the primary mechanism by which the SCM confuses itself (insofar as it realistically does nothing more than blame an individual) comes by way of the *latent condition* and its default conversion into a so-called *organisational accident* (I say blame since its remedial strategies are wholly misdirected).

Reason claims to be able to distinguish between an organisational accident and an individual one. However, clear from everything above (not least Reason's own work), there are only individual accidents and that is a fact that the most ardent SCM supporter cannot now deny. The organisational accident, a wholly flawed concept irrespective of aggregation, is therefore an academic invention; a nonexistent. As such, the latent condition does no more than attempt to transfer blame (by way only of the merely conditional) from one individual to another en route to its inevitable, invariable and unconditional conclusion that the organisation caused the accident.

To convert an individual accident into an organisational one according to the SCM requires nothing more than the existence of a non-causative condition (there being no such thing as a *causative* condition of course). But, and irrespective of whether root cause is presumed to reside upstream or not, the requisite condition will always exist; indeed, ill-informed models such as the SCM, *always and only*, find conditions and wholly irrelevant non-transitive causes that appear to them as combinatorial explosions of possible root causes. Consequently, any individual accident, whether by way of the impossible or the confused, can always be re-labelled as an organisational one according to the SCM philosophy; as such, the upstream transference of blame is guaranteed, irrespective of whether that guarantee comes by way of coincidence or a flawed notion of invariable and unconditional sequence.

Regardless of Reason's effective denial regarding where and why the antecedent causal chain must logically be cut short, he is fully aware that a condition cannot be a cause; however, he appears not to have fully grasped the difference between the two. Consequently, the mechanism by which he feels justified in advising industry to move beyond the barrier that is the deliberate act must be assumed to be unknowingly flawed to him; that is, he is unaware that the resident pathogen metaphor results in the persistent ignorance of the natural break that identifies the limit of the proximate causal search. Therefore, Reason's acknowledgement that the latent condition is unacceptably vague, problematic and far from workable may have been more than just understatement; it could have been the voice of confirmation, staring the obvious in the face but feeling compelled to deny it. Furthermore, we know that the SCM's invariable and unconditional sequence (expressed by way of its general philosophy, the organisation accident and the latent condition) compels itself to see all causes and conditions, always and without exception, as being transitive. However, and quite remarkably, Reason *et al* (2006:16) fully agree that such an invariable and unconditional sequence is *"logically invalid"*!

Whilst that statement is, indeed, remarkable, the reason they feel able to make it only becomes clear when we realise that they do so during a brief discussion on Hume's *post hoc fallacy*. From that, it is clear that Reason et al (2006) believe that if a causal sequence appears complex (i.e. SCM like or web like as opposed to linear or normative), they are at liberty to ignore the need for causes to be transitive. Of course, if they were to accept Hume (and, by default, Hart & Honore 2002 and the relevant argument herein), they would be disproving the SCM; that is, they would be acknowledging that it is the SCM's arbitrarily selected 'stop rule' itself that is *logically invalid*. Consequently, they would also be acknowledging that the notions of the organisational accident and the latent condition are also *logically invalid.*

Nonetheless, Reason et al (2006:13) have said that the SCM is *"irrefutable by standard scientific methods"* and that *"no crucial experiment"* exists to *"reject the model"*. However, in light of everything herein, those views, clearly, need formally withdrawing. Indeed, the most that Reason *et al* (2006) ought really to have said is that *they* have been unable to reject and disprove the SCM. Of course, given numerous inaccuracies, contradictions and fundamental flaws, it is unlikely that many SCM's supporters will ever accept what is wrong with it; indeed, the Titanic sails on (e.g. Reason 2008).

The latent condition aspires to be a root cause; that was Reason's own claim and we cannot be distracted from that by Reason *et al's* (2006) belated and underspecified denial; changing the label on the tin does not alter its contents and it does not alter the result of its use either. For all intents and purposes, Reason's work in the context here relates exclusively to causation. Therefore, his openly declared decision not to become embroiled in a debate on the philosophy (let alone reality) of causation was disappointing, to say the least; indeed, for many (TYS), it negated all of his critical comments on the subject.

The reason that accidents **do not** happen in the way that the SCM assumes is because they **cannot happen** in that way; consequently, it is little wonder that the SCM persistently communicates a flawed and counter-productive message. With its philosophy rendered absurd and ridiculous by giants in the relevant fields, its so-called indicators (nothing more than Bird's originals or Tripod's® later ones perhaps) reveal it to be nothing more than a workplace inspection or audit checklist devoid, not least, of analytical, diagnostic, explanatory, investigative or predictive capability. Nonetheless, in the face of numerous problems, Reason et al (2006:16) offer that the SCM is now an accident model that describes *how* an accident *could happen*.

Whilst that is as absurd as any other offering, it is yet another massive contradiction. Both Hollnagel (2004:53) and Reason (2004:15) have made the ridiculous statement that there is no starting point in any accident; i.e. they believe that the causative search can always be taken one or more steps further back....even as far back as the big bang! But, in order to describe *how* an accident *could happen*, they would need to contradict themselves and specify, not least, a starting point. Of course, and as we know, that contradictory starting point is, invariably and unconditionally, the organisation; that is, Reason has indeed specified his own (albeit wholly unsupportable) "clear cut" rule for "restricting such retrospective searches". But, if the causative search can always be taken one or more steps further back, there is no logical reason, beyond a flawed and default view of cause, to specify *any* starting point; indeed, any *stopping* point. As an aside, by virtue of a literal analysis of their own beliefs therefore, the organisation can *never* be the cause of an accident; recall also that Bogner (2004), fully aligned to the SCM, contradicts the view that organisations cause all accidents even though she is moving still further away from the heart of the problem and into the realms of the regulator (note, of course, that she does so in the same error-laden condition that Reason does).

In describing *how* an accident *could happen*, we know that an SCM analysis of that hypothetical accident would be compelled to arrive at a finding of management as the cause. In addition, we know that the identification of management or the organisation as the cause is compelled, or forced, by way of the flawed mechanism that is the latent condition. But, all downstream causes and conditions would need to be transitive for that finding to be valid and we know that such a standard, invariably and unconditionally, cannot be met. Consequently, the SCM cannot possibly suggest how an accident *could happen* because, quite simply and irrefutably, they cannot happen in the way it assumes; indeed, once we accept that causes must be transitive and that the SCM stop rule is flawed, it should be obvious that, either way in the causative search (i.e. upstream or downstream), the organisation cannot possibly, ever, be a root or proximate cause.

Alternatively, assume, irrespective of its confusion (if that is at all possible), that the SCM *might* be able to predict *how* an accident *could happen*; in so doing, recall that the SCM now claims *not* to be identifying root causes. Unfortunately, we can go no further since that poses an immediate and obvious question; how can a model tell us *how* an accident *could happen* yet, paradoxically, be unable to tell us what will cause it? If the reader pauses for a moment it will become blatantly obvious that to describe *how* an accident *could happen* without mentioning, implying or alluding to cause is impossible. All that springs immediately to mind to solve this enigma is that the SCM would be citing items from a workplace audit or inspection checklist. That is all it could do without contradicting its belated, and quite ridiculous, denial relating to root cause.

As it is, academics have pondered relentlessly over just exactly *what* a latent condition is. Of course, *it* does not exist in reality. Reason's notion of the latent conditions or holes in the barriers or slices of cheese appearing and disappearing are statements of the obvious that can only possibly relate to short lived and intermittent conditions, errors or violations. That said, given that the SCM sequence is invariable and unconditional, shouldn't those holes, actually therefore, always be accidents? They cannot possibly relate to the more long term conditions or errors that were involved, for instance and allegedly, with disasters such as Challenger or the Deepwater Horizon. If they did, they would naturally become static and identifiable. That is, the SCM (in so-called diagnostic or Tripod mode perhaps) would surely identify them before the loss occurred; unless, of course, they are, indeed, only 'identifiable'...in retrospect.

Mysteriously, the holes only become static and obvious *after* the accident has occurred. But, if they weren't static and identifiable before the event, how can they possibly be so now? Of course, and in reality, the holes in the slices of cheese or barriers exist only after the accident has happened. As retrospective figments of the SCM investigator's imagination, they are created by him as he back tracks, breaking every rule known to man, through the antecedent causal chain (indeed, an investigation is unnecessary since a post-accident inspection or audit would do the same insofar as everything negative that could possibly be found would count as a root cause according to him). Having identified the deliberate act, confirmation bias reigns supreme and he finds the inevitable and compulsory conditions by which the move away from the proximate cause is enabled and justified according to his view of cause.

Of course, and in effect, latent conditions are nothing more than the modern day equivalent of the emperor's new clothes; they exist, as do fairies, only for those who believe in them (that said, belief in fairies is insufficient for either science or commonsense, such a belief must be based on observation). Unfortunately, all that gets generated by the SCM is a potentially infinite list (limited only by an arbitrary, inconsistent and subjective choice) of things and occurrences that, had they not been there or occurred, might possibly have prevented the accident; however, and as we know, that does nothing for the central causal enquiry...nothing at all. Furthermore, it does nothing for the remedial strategy since, in belated denial of root cause, the effect of the intervention cannot be measured; even if it could, and aware that it would be found to be ineffective, the SCM defends itself by saying that the next accident was totally different. Even as a so-called diagnostic tool, the SCM is also pointless since it identifies non-causative factors; i.e. it identifies things that exist regardless of whether an accident occurs or not.

The search for the so-called a priori set of indicators necessary to support the resident pathogen metaphor and off-set the fact that the SCM could only be wise after the event was never going to be successful; whilst that failure alone disproves the SCM, Reason effectively leaves in place a theory of accident proneness for senior managers. Tripod's® use and unwitting incorporation of the latent failure (i.e. latent condition) was ill-informed and misguided; clearly, Tripod identifies conditions. Furthermore, its development teams 'understanding' of the latent failure as expressed in the short section above was thoroughly confused and, in any event, different to Reason's own confused understanding of it. For instance, recall that Reason (1990; 2003:152) said that "*latent conditions*" were "*General Failure Types in Tripod parlance*" but that he (2004:134) also said that "*GFTs, in turn, create the conditions that promote or exacerbate unsafe acts*". Consequently, given the true nature of the latent condition, those statements reveal a nonsensical circularity.

In effect, the development teams simply re-labelled hundreds of so-called indicators as latent failures and then (having convinced themselves) asked industry to accept that they had now both confirmed and validated the notion of the latent failure and its very existence (in reality, they might just as well have labelled everything as slices of bread and cheese and claimed that all workplaces are full of cheese sandwiches); indeed, the worst example or definition of a self-fulfilling prophecy if not tautology springs uncontrollably to mind. Call it what you will but workplaces are full of inert, lifeless, non-causative conditions, not cheese sandwiches or latent failures.

Blaming management and then defaulting to the post-accident conditional sanitising of workplaces is, invariably and unconditionally, leaving the proximate cause unaddressed. Indeed, the pre-accident sanitisation or safety proofing of our environments is not preventing accidents and never will whilst man has an option to decide on his behaviour. However, if man is to maintain his dignity, autonomy and earning capacity then some might need to wake up to the fact that no robot ever needed to join a trade union.

Perfectly understandably, Professor Reason has been unable to disprove his own premise (of course, confirmation bias is a powerful phenomenon, especially when the core belief is well engrained). Indeed, given the support for the SCM and its premise from academics around the world who have also been unable to disprove it, some could be forgiven for believing in its robustness. However, and Difford's (1998) original rejection aside, the fact that it has been so readily disproved here does not assist any understanding of those inabilities. Consequently, many academics, institutions, organisations and professional journals worldwide should be asking themselves some very searching questions; not least, the Parliamentary Office of Science and Technology should seriously review the declaration that it makes on its POST publications. As for the UK HSE, they have much to explain I feel.

Reason et al (2006:16) fully accept that accidents will happen even when everything required of the organisation is in place; yet, they say that the SCM can only identify *how* an accident *must happen* when just such a fully compliant situation exists. Clearly, that statement sums up everything that is currently wrong in this field. What they are saying in effect is that when everything required of the organisation is in place, the SCM will be able to find something by which causative responsibility can be directly attributed to it; whilst that is an impossibility, that is exactly what the SCM does.

Chapter Seven:
Difford's New Millennium Theory

I do not intend to conclude here in the way that some academics for instance may be accustomed. The interim summaries have dealt with most things and, in any event, this book must be studied and absorbed. Hopefully, it emphasises why the models etc under the spotlight are so critically flawed in so many areas.

This book has taken nine long months to produce and is the result of fourteen years of associated research. Hundreds of references and pages have been removed at the Institute's request to ensure clarity for the end user for whom the text primarily exists to inform and I am indebted to Trevor Williams. Data was also extracted from a number of my presentations and reports and continuity and consistency may have suffered in one or two places as a result. However, the essence is unaffected. It is my own unaided work and I am fully responsible for it. Neucom Ltd will provide a platform on its web site so that I might respond immediately to any findings, criticisms or challenges as, and howsoever, they might arise; this, so that purchasers and IIAI Members can be updated as quickly as possible. Furthermore, that will allow me, should the need arise, to air those additional findings in support that, at this time, are deemed unnecessary by the Institute.

Petersen's (1971;1978) Multiple Causation Theory

According to Petersen (1971:13)....

"...we know that behind every accident there lie many contributing factors, causes and subcauses.

That part of his statement is not wholly inaccurate. However, those factors etc are part of the antecedent causal chain, they are not causes for the purposes of our causal enquiries; they are things that we either ignore or work through to find *the cause*. The failure by writers such as Petersen, Bird and Reason to recognise this fact is the sole reason for their belief that the causal chain in any accident can be traced back until the dawn of time itself; indeed, it is not a belief, it is a fact. It results in numerous (potentially infinite) so-called root causes being identified, compels such writers to see all accidents as 'causatively' different and removes any predictive capability; indeed, it effectively renders accidents unpreventable. However, whilst those factors etc are found to invariably exist post-accident, the accident is not compelled upon their existence. Consequently, causes are not being identified and the above part of Petersen's statement does not support his theory.

Petersen (1971:13) goes on to say that...

"...The theory of multiple causation is that these factors combine together in random fashion, causing accidents". **If this is true**, *our investigation of accidents ought to identify some of these factors - as many as possible...".*

That is not true and has been formally rejected and disproved here, above and below. Whilst contrary to empirical data and findings in the field, it forms part of an exceptionless statement of cause by Petersen that simply cannot be met. For it to be true, my preceding paragraph above would have to be false. However, for that to be false requires that we see all conditions as causes and that we ignore the barrier that the deliberate act logically presents between causes that are properly transitive and those that are merely part of the antecedent causal chain.

Already noted in the introduction, neither Petersen nor Bird embarked on any form of discussion in the purely causal context. Consequently, it is assumed that Petersen was unaware that his theory was wholly and inadvertently reliant on non-causal factors. It relies on the use of a 'faulty calculator' insofar as any natural break in the causal chain has to be patched or linked by a mere condition; of course, such theories hold true only in the eyes of those who concoct them and only then when all natural, logical and commonsense notions of cause are ignored. However, to posit a notion of causation that is utterly reliant on things that are not causes is, in the words of those who would also refute the no free-will argument, to render yourself ridiculous.

Petersen has also said that *"An unsafe act, an unsafe condition, an accident: all these are symptoms of something wrong in the management system"*. That is irrefutably wrong. Such a statement conceals the fact that the theory is wholly reliant, notwithstanding that above, on an arbitrarily selected and indefensible 'stop-rule' (if not start rule). There is no more reason to halt the causative search at the upper echelons of the organisation than there is to halt it at the point in time when the great, great, great grand-mother of the perpetrator first laid eyes on a butterfly.

Bird's (1974) Updated Sequence

Insofar as Bird's sequence might represent a theory on the causes of accidents, it is rejected and disproved for the same reasons cited at Petersen plus those here, above and below.

Heinrich's unnecessary depiction of his theory as a row of dominoes was misleading. It was over specified and encouraged those who would follow it to install multiple dominoes or slices of cheese into their models without realising that there was, if fact, no basis to follow suit. As a result, they typically installed 5 components and were then compelled to invent the respective labels without any evidence whatsoever regarding any causal relationship; indeed, all evidence was, and remains to be, to the contrary.

Bird said that...

"Re-emphasis is directed to the fact that the domino effect is not necessarily a direct chain reaction involved with single events. It is rather a reaction involving the potential of multiple events at each stage, with each established causal factor capable of continuing the

reaction itself and of interacting with other factors to continue the domino effect".

Reason fell into the same trap as regards his belief in a combinatorial explosion of possible root causes; however, apparent causal complexity results from attempts to construct cause from amidst numerous (potentially infinite) non-causal conditions. The trap is avoided when we realise that cause is not constructed, it is found.

Linear sequencing is the result of the investigator's work post-accident to concisely explain and describe the sequence for practical purposes. The sequence in 'reality' may appear complex to the unwary or inexperienced; it also appears complex when causes are confused with conditions and when unworkable and unrealistic stop rules are enforced. Nonetheless, for each identified factor to be shown to have logically resulted in the accident, those multiple factors must each be over-lapping or transitive in the true and proper causal sense. It makes no difference whether those factors are imagined as being linearly aligned, adjacent to each other or configured in some other fanciful or web-like way. Hume's warning (post hoc fallacy) is a statement to the unwary regarding the potential to confuse coincidental relationships with those that are properly, logically and demonstrably causal. It cannot be invariably and unconditionally ignored by, nor is there a separate rule for or available to, those whose theories or models are disproved without it.

Reason's (1997;2004) Swiss cheese model

In light of this book, the SCM model and theory is rejected. Reliant on Heinrich, it restated Petersen and Bird and, as such or not, fails on the same points as them and they on essentially the same points as it. Confronted with the problems that Petersen and Bird ignored, Reason presumed to 'justify' a persistent tracing of cause to management via his resident pathogen metaphor; that claims to be able to find proximate cause at the wrong end of the antecedent causal chain and its philosophy and mechanism 'enables' this without exception. As a result, the organisation (i.e. a non-causative, non-entity or thing) is causative of all accidents; however, that is simply not possible.

Many have spent years pondering the latent condition when the right question was...*why* is it needed? When academic verbosity is reduced to a lay intelligible answer to that, the SCM collapses. It has always shown the accident trajectory starting at senior management. But, if that *was* its belief and all causes *were*, as posited, always transitive, there was no need for the latent condition since the transitive link from 'rubble' to organisation would be obvious and defensible; of course, the link is neither obvious nor defensible since it is simply not possible. Consequently, the latent condition, a desperate concoction, reduces to a fiction that was designed to achieve the impossible.

Whilst the basis of that fiction may have been difficult for some to unravel, it would not be (and has not been) difficult for experts in the relevant field. Unfortunately, and despite believing the SCM to be irrefutable by standard scientific methods and that no crucial experiment existed to reject the model, Reason avoids discussing causation. However, given that his claims contradict the foundations of causation since Hume, he should have embraced the opportunity to explain why so many had got it so categorically and irrefutably wrong; of course, the fact that he did not is, now perhaps, self-evident.

According to Reason *et al*, there are multiple 'versions' and uses of the SCM. However, they state that the SCM (*in the singular*) is irrefutable. Consequently, devoid of distinct premises etc. pre-dating 2006 and specifying when, where, how and by whom each version had been declared irrefutable, the disproving of one disproves all. If the claim was just Reason *et als*, it was naive; if it was the academic community's then they should temper their readiness to comment on matters now clearly beyond them. The central version (not that I need specify it) is disproved and I therefore say that the SCM in any guise is disproved. I do not believe in multiple versions and, in any event, changing the 'label on the tin' alters neither its contents, over-riding philosophy nor effect of its use. The shelf-life of the Swiss cheese model expired long ago; indeed, it was never fit for consumption.

Heinrich's (1931;1941) Accident Sequence

Whilst rejected by many, Heinrich's theory has never been refuted. However, and whilst I am fully supportive of its essence, he too put forward an exceptionless statement of cause by way of a contradictory allusion to a proximate cause beyond that which he could either practically, logically or demonstrably have found. He could no more have found heredity to be the proximate cause of the accidents in his study than Petersen, Bird or Reason could find management or the organisation; his upstream dominoes therefore represent an 'option' on the antecedent causal chain. As a result, his dominoes represent an over specification insofar as there is factual ground for only two. In addition, he placed a percentage of accident causes in the potentially debatable and, hence, potentially undecided category of unsafe conditions that should have been assigned to unsafe acts.

Having analysed his work closely, I do not believe that Heinrich would disapprove of the text herein. In view of his hope that this millennium would find industry both able and informed enough to properly consider the underlying field of human behaviour, I feel he would also have approved of the title, The New Millennium Theory.

Difford's (2010) New Millennium Theory

The New Millennium Theory is offered in the hope that it will assist the accident preventionist. It *cannot* co-exist with the critical offerings of Petersen, Bird and Reason and is therefore a statement that their models and theories are categorically rejected and disproved.

No component of the their relevant work can remain if we are to guarantee a commonsense approach to causation in the context here. That said, it is Professor Reason's academic work that is responsible for the perpetuation of the management failure myth and the task to argue against the reality of the organisational accident and resident pathogen metaphor as presented herein is his, and his alone. I therefore look forward to either a letter of thanks from him or to addressing his responses on-line or in person at one of the conferences that Neucom Ltd will organise to explore this book's contents further (there being far more beneath it than has been installed here).

Importantly, the attack herein is upon the SCM and its premise, not its author. The problem for industry and huge swathes of the academic community at the moment is to first overcome its groundless obsession with organisational failings and its reluctance, driven by appeals to emotion and regulatory self-interest, to confront the behavioural problem; the organisation is the breeding ground for the cure, not the disease. I am a personal supporter of the basis of Professor Reason's early work in error modelling (some of which is still mandatory reading on certain IIAI courses) and it is a shame that he was persuaded away from it; fortunately, many were not. Nonetheless, the organisational accident is a miscalculated fiction born of a mistaken belief in the latent condition. A non-entity such as an organisation, management *per se* or a system cannot cause an accident and you cannot trace cause to *it* beyond the proximate cause that is the deliberate act.

Therefore, in view of everything above and for now, I will say this...

Unpredictable and uncontrollable consequences of natural phenomena aside, human behaviour, suitably defined, will be the underlying cause of any accident.

By way of assistance...

Knowledge of both outcome and underlying cause aside, the finer detail desired by many causal enquiries is impossible to specify with any certainty.

Events are reconstructed post-accident but, cause is not constructed.

The link between the relevant outcome and its underlying cause must be demonstrably and/or logically transitive.

An investigation claiming to have found multiple immediate and underlying causes has been misdirected and is incomplete.

A non-human such as an organisation or a system cannot be an underlying cause.

Underlying cause is found where the antecedent or non-transitive causes end and the transitive causes begin.

The behaviour of a man who has been found to be the underlying cause of an accident is attributable only to him and responsibility for any transitively traceable outcome is his as regards the central causal enquiry.

Organisations with systems that are in full legal compliance and that achieve 100% in their audit returns are (in the context here) simply awaiting an injury producing or environment damaging accident.

Fig.NMT. below is provided to assist a mental image of the reality of the causes of accidents; that said, if a picture is needed after all that has been said then we may need to return to page 1. and read over.

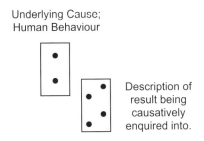

Underlying Cause;
Human Behaviour

Description of result being causatively enquired into.

The Final Discussion Here

I do not expect to alter the views of certain people in respects of the above discussions. The effects of appeals to emotion, self-interest, escalation of commitment, group think, hindsight bias and confirmation bias are amongst the many problems that will obstruct any such change of view. Not least, factions of the academic community seem intent on keeping the focus of attention off of the critical problem and they are, in the UK for certain, supported by the Health & Safety Executive. That said, it is not so much the absurd models and theories themselves as the philosophy that they promote that must be disposed of. Unfortunately, the disproving of a theory is not enough since the remedy for its infection will not suit all.

Thankfully, the reader's views on causation are immaterial since the mechanism that exists for those who will seek it compels an investigator to logically verify his findings...whatever they are. Directors and senior managers will be able to instruct investigators with confidence since it makes no difference how many so-called root causes appear to emerge. The attendant statement is simple, "present any cause that you like but, be prepared to logically and demonstrably confirm it as having been *the cause*...in the singular". Amongst many other things, the tools provided enable a plain English classification of human behaviour and promote a deeper understanding of the type of remedial intervention strategies that may need to be developed or considered in order to improve its prediction, detection and control. In addition, Directors and Senior Managers involved in the field trials reported a massive improvement in the resulting reports. In particular, a tempering of tone and overall stance was evidenced as a much clearer and firmer (or confident) dividing line between those findings that were critical, and those that were not. Indeed, the general views reported to the TYS were that the singular most insurmountable obstruction presented to those tasked with the defence of the organisation was finally being justifiably eroded away.

That said, I have been requested by two international institutions to leave the requisite mechanism out of this particular text since the unanimous view was that it should be supported by on-line and/or class-room training from properly qualified and experienced instructors. Similarly, the analytical tool required to properly classify and address the behavioural aspects uncovered during an investigation would be open to misuse if released here for unguided general consumption (the same applies to the software that will also be available to support both). However, I will say this. We are now into the second Ten Year Study and an on-going theme of research over the past fourteen years has included analysis of the so-called human factors programs. In the main, such programs, which include those purporting to place organisations on journeys towards an accident free status, have been found to contain common critical flaws. This book, all relevant research and data point undeniably to behavioural problems that are beyond the control of the current organisational approach in the same way that the behaviour of recent (August 2011) rioters in the UK for instance is beyond the control of either their parents or the government. However, the off-the-shelf packages that are so quickly compiled by those with little or no industrial experience and an ill-informed view of the cause of the problem that actually needs to be addressed are confounding the very problem that they claim to be able to assist.

Each UK rioter, as do we all in our social and working environments, made a free and conscious decision regarding his behaviour. On the one side, according to Bentham, he had the chain of causes and effects leading to that point in time. However, on the other, he had the God given right to choose, ultimately and for his own benefit, between two extremes of behaviour. Of course, those two extremes reduce to nought but the difference between that which is knowingly right, and that which is knowingly wrong. As the judge in *R* v *Norwest* said, nobody can resile from having to make a realistic and commonsense assessment of what he did that day. When we heed those words, we find that very few men have ever caused another man's behaviour; certainly, no organisation in the context here has ever caused it.

APPENDICES

Appendix 1:
The SCM – Communicating a Flawed Message

Applying the SCM in practice is highly problematic. For instance, during the TYS, 7 in-house investigators who were familiar with the use of the SCM were given the same accident details (including all necessary supporting documents and photographs) and asked to conduct a secondary analysis of it; three others who had received training in a derivative RCA software did likewise. Five other investigators used basic investigative tools and methods and took on average 12 hours to arrive at more or less identical conclusions. The other ten, who also worked separately, took between 35 and 55 hours to complete things and no two produced even remotely similar conclusions; this, despite all of them having essentially identified the same, numerous, latent conditions. In light of this and the many other problems with the SCM, Reason et al's (2006) view that it supports explanation and communication is unsupported. Practical and experimental use of the SCM has categorically proven but one thing; the SCM is capable only of communicating its own view of causation. If its notion of cause is flawed then, by default, it communicates a flawed message and misdirects resources.

Appendix 2:
Difford's Behavioural Research

Whilst the useable output of Difford's behaviour based research will be incorporated into other texts, his position should be clarified. Whilst supportive of the essence of behavioural safety, he has been highly critical of certain off-the-shelf packages. He feels, for instance, that initiatives based on notions of accident free workplaces (an impossibility according to him) are doomed to fail. Indeed, most organisations that had signed up to such reported feeling as though they had been left holding the baby (TYS; some reported that they had been left with nothing at all). He feels that such initiatives cannot be driven from the top down and that consultants attach the 'top down label' in order to be able to blame the largely inevitable failure of the program on a so-called loss of management commitment. As a warning to both safety practitioners and directors alike, Difford offers that 'if it seems attractive to you, it is highly unlikely to be attractive (hence effective) to the target audience'.

Appendix 3:
Who's Leading Who?

As it happens, the UK HSE were heavily involved with the production of that publication so as to, in their words, "ensure compatibility with existing HSE guidance" (HSE 2004e). However, some might have expected a body such as the British Standards Institute to have based their beliefs on numerous factually worked examples of their own rather than, as it appears they did, follow the lead of others.

REFERENCES

BOOKS

Ashworth, A. (1999). Principle of Criminal Law. 3rd Edition. Oxford, Oxford University Press.

Bamber, L. (1996). Principles of the Management of Risk. In (Ed) Ridley, J. Safety at Work. 4th Edition. Oxford, Butterworth-Heinemann.

Beyer, D.S. (1916). Industrial Accident Prevention. Boston, Houghton Mifflin Company.

Bignell, V. and Fortune, J. (1984). Understanding Systems Failures. Manchester, Manchester University Press.

Bird, F.E. Jnr. (1974). Management Guide to Loss Control. Georgia, Institute press.

Bird, F.E., Jnr and Germain, G.L. (1966) Damage Control: A New Horizon in Accident Prevention and Cost Improvement. American Management Association. USA.

Botham. T. (2008). Agent-Causation Revisited: Origination and Contemporary Theories of Free Will. Saarbrucken, VDM Verlag.

Burns, J.H. and Hart, H.L.A. (1996). The Collected Works of Jeremy Bentham. An Introduction to the Principles of Morals and Legislation. USA, Oxford University Press.

Cambon, J., Guarnieri, F. and Goeneweg, J. (2006). Towards a new tool for measuring Safety Management Systems performance. In (Eds) Hollnagel, E. and Rigaud, E. Proceedings of the Second Resilience Engineering Symposium. Fr, Transvalor Presses de Mines.

Christoffel T. & Gallagher, S.C. (2006). Injury Prevention and Public Health: Practical Knowledge, Skills and Strategies. 2nd Edition. Sudbury MA, Jones and Bartlett Publishers Inc.

Collingwood, R.G. (1940). An Essay on Metaphysics. Oxford, Clarendon Press.

Dekker, S. (2002). The field guide to Human Error Investigations. Aldershot, Ashgate.

Difford, P. (1998/2004). These references relate to summaries of reports presented to the IIAI Executive Committee and members should not confuse the Difford (1998) reference with his 1998 RDC Projects Report prepared for the Executive to determine research for the 2000-2002 period.

IIAI Ten Year Study, 98-08 and 09-to date. These findings will not be available in published form until finalised.

Duncan, D.F. (1988) Epidemiology: Basis for Disease Prevention and Health promotion. New York, McMillan.

Firenze, R.J. (1973). Guide to Occupational safety and Health; with Readings on Industrial Hazard Control. Dubuque, Kendall-Hunt.

Ferry, T.S. (1988). Modern Accident Investigation and Analysis. 2nd Edition. Chichester, John Wiley & Sons.

Feyer, A-M. and Williamson, A.M. (1998). Human Factors in Accident Modelling. In Ed Jeanne Mager Stellman. Encyclopaedia of Occupational Health and Safety. 4th Edition, Vol II. Geneva, International Labour Office.

Fleming, J.G. (1961) The Law of Torts. 2nd Edition. Sydney, Law Book Co.

Friedman, G.D. (1987). Primer of Epidemiology. New York, McGraw-Hill. Web of causation for myocardial infarction.

Galileo Galilei (1632). Dialogue Concerning the Two Chief World Systems. Drake, S. (1992) translator. Los Angeles, University of California Press.

Green, M.D., Freedman, D.M. and Gordis, L. (2000). Reference Guide on Epidemiology. In Reference Manual on Scientific Evidence. 2nd Edition. Washington, Federal Judicial Center.

Greenwood, (Major) and Woods, H.M. (1953). The Incidence of Industrial Accidents Upon Individuals: with Special Reference to Multiple Accidents. London, HMSO.

Gottfredson, M.R. and Hirschi, T. (1990). A General Theory of Crime. Stanford, Stanford University Press.

Gullotta, T.P. and Bloom, M. (Eds) (2003) Encyclopaedia of Primary Prevention and Health Promotion. London, Kluwer Academic/Plenum Publishers.

Haddon, W., Suchman, E.A. and Klein, D. (Eds) (1964). Accident Research: Methods and Approaches. New York, Harper and Row.

Hale, A.R. and Perusse, M. (1977). Attitude to Safety-Facts and Assumptions. In Ed Phillips, J. Safety at Work; Recent Research into the Causes and Prevention of Industrial Accidents. Oxford, Centre for Socio-Legal Studies.

Hart, H.L.A. and Honore, T. (2002). Causation in the Law. 2nd Edition. Oxford, Clarendon Press.

Heinrich, H.W. (1931). Industrial Accident Prevention: A Scientific Approach. New York, McGraw-Hill.

Heinrich, H.W. (1941). Industrial Accident Prevention: A Safety Management Approach. 2nd Edition. New York, McGraw-Hill.

Heinrich, H.W. (1950). Industrial Accident Prevention: A Safety Management Approach. 3rd Edition. New York, McGraw-Hill.

Heinrich, H.W. (1959). Industrial Accident Prevention: A Safety Management Approach. 4th Edition. New York, McGraw-Hill.

Heinrich, H.W. Petersen, D., and Roos, N. (1980). Industrial Accident Prevention: A Scientific Approach. 5th Edition. New York, McGraw-Hill.

HilgenKamp, K. (2006). Environmental Health-Ecological Perspectives. Ontario, Jones and Bartlett Publishers.

Hollin, C.R. (2002). Psychology and Crime. East Sussex, Routledge.

Hollnagel, E. (2004). Barriers and Accident Prevention. Aldershot, Ashgate Publishing Ltd.

HSE (1978). One Hundred Fatal Accidents in Construction. HMSO.

HSE (1985). A Deadly Maintenance. HMSO.

IISE (1986). Agricultural Black Spot. HMSO.

HSE (1988). Blackspot Construction. HMSO.

HSE (1989). HSG48. Human Factors in Industrial Safety. 2nd Impression. HSE/ HMSO.

HSE (1991). Successful Health and Safety Management. UK, HMSO.

HSE (1997a). HSG65. Successful Health and Safety Management. HSE Books.

HSE (1997b). HS(G)96: The Costs of Accidents at Work. HMSO.

HSE (2000). HSG65. Successful Health and Safety Management. HSE Books.

HSE (1998). Individual Differences in Accident Liability: A Review. CRR175. HSE Books.

HSE (2001). Accident Investigation: The Drivers Methods and Outcomes. CRR 344/201. HSE Books.

HSE (2002). Techniques for Addressing Rule Violations in the off-shore industries. Offshore Technology Report 2000/096. HSE Books.

HSE (2003a). Reducing Error and Influencing Behaviour: HSG48. HSE Books.

HSE (2003b). Successful Health and Safety Management. HSG65. HSE Books.

HSE (2003c). "Safety report assessment guide: explosives". HSE Books.

HSE (2003d). Causal factors in construction accidents. RR 156. HSE Books.

HSE (2003e). HSG65. Successful Health and Safety Management. HSE Books.

HSE (2004a). Improving health and safety in construction-Phase 2-Depth and breadth-Volume 1-Summary report. Research Report 231. HSE Books.

HSE (2004b). Improving health and safety in construction-Phase 2-Depth and breadth-Volume 5-Falls from height. Research Report 234. HSE Books.

HSE (2004c). Recidivist Risk Takers Who Work at Height. Research Report 201. HSE Books.

HSE (2004d). HSG245. Investigating Accidents and Incidents: A workbook for employers, unions, safety representatives and safety professionals. HSE Books.

HSE (2004e). Operational Circular OC 203/12.

HSE (2005). Trends and Context to Rates of Workplace Injury. RR 386. HSE Books.

HSE (2006). Manual Handling Incidents Data Base: A compilation and analysis of offshore industry reports. HSE Books.

HSE (2007). Management of Health and Safety at Work: Management of Health and Safety at Work Regulations 1999 Approved Code of Practice and Guidance (L21). 2nd Edition. HSE Books.

HSE (2009a). HSG65. Successful Health and Safety Management. HSE Books.

HSE (2009b). HSG48: Reducing Error and Influencing Behaviour: HSE Books.

Hume, D. (1739-40) (1969). A Treatise of Human Nature. London. Penguin Books.

Ivamy, E,R.H. (1993). General Principles of Insurance Law. 6th Edition. Butterworth-Heineman.

Janis, I.L. (1982). Groupthink: Psychological Studies of Policy Decisions and Fiascoes. Belmont, Cengage Learning.

Jones, E.E., and Nisbett, R.E. (1972). The Actor and the Observer: divergent perceptions of the causes of behaviour. In Eds Jones, E.E., Kanouse, D., Kelley, H.H., Nisbett, R,E., Valins, S. and Weiner, B. Attribution: Perceiving the Causes of Behaviour. Morristown, General Learning Press.

Kalis, P.J., Reiter, T.M. and Segerdahl, J.R. (1997). Policy Holder's Guide to the Law of Insurance Coverage. Llf Ed. Aspen Publishers. (2004 supp via GoogleBooks).

Kohn, L.T., Corrigan, J. and Donaldson, M.S. (Eds) (2003). To Err is Human; building a safer health system. Washington, National Academy Press.

Lateiner, A. and Heinrich, H.W. (1969). Management and Controlling Employee Performance. New York, Enterprise Press.

Lingard, H. and Rowlinson, S.M. (2005). Occupational Health and Safety in Construction Project Management. Abingdon, Spon Press.

Lombroso, C (1911) Crime: Its causes and remedies. London, Heinemann. As translated by Horton, H. P.

Lowe. E.J. (2002). A Survey of Metaphysics. Oxford, Oxford University Press.

Luttwak, E.N. (1976). The Grand Strategy of the Roman Empire: From the First Century A.D. to the Third. London and Baltimore, The John Hopkins University Press.

Machiavelli, N. (1513). The Prince. New York, Dover Publications Inc as translated (1992).

Mackie, J.L. (1993). In Eds Sosa, E. and Tooley, M. (1993). Causation. Oxford, Oxford University Press.

MacMahon, B. Pugh, T.F. and Ipsen, J. (1960). Epidemiologic Methods. Boston, Little, Brown and Co.

Mill, S.J. (1843). A System of Logic. Google Books.

Nemeth, C.P. (Ed) (2008). Improving Healthcare team Communication: Building on Lessons from Aviation and Aerospace. Aldershot, Ashgate.

O'Brien, W.H., Kaplar, M.E. and McGrath, J.J. (2004). Broadly Based Causal Models of Behaviour Disorders. In Eds Hersey, M., Haynes, S.N. and Heiby, E.M. Comprehensive Handbook of Psychological Assessment. Vol 3. Behavioural Assessment. John Wiley & Sons Inc. Hoboken, New Jersey.

O'Connor, T. (1995). Agent Causation. In eds O'Connor, T. Agents, Causes and Events: Essays on Indeterminism and Free Will. New York, Oxford University Press.

O'Connor, T. (2002). Persons & Causes: The Metaphysics of Free Will. Oxford, Oxford University Press.

Petersen, D. (1971). Techniques of Safety Management. New York, McGraw-Hill.

Petersen, D. (1978). Techniques of Safety Management. 2nd Edition. New York, McGraw-Hill.

Popper, K. (2002). The Logic of Scientific Discovery. 2nd Edition. London & New York, Routledge.

Raouf, A. (1998). Theory of Accident Causes. In Ed Jeanne Mager Stellman. Encyclopaedia of Occupational Health and Safety. 4th Edition, Vol II. Geneva, International Labour Office.

Reason, J. (2003). Human Error. Cambridge, Cambridge University Press.

Reason (2004). Managing the Risks of Organizational Accidents. Aldershot, Ashgate Publishing Ltd.

Reason, J. (2008). The Human Contribution. Farnham, Ashgate Publishing.

Reid, T. (1764). In (Ed) Wright, G.N. (1843). Essays on the Active Powers of the Human Mind an Inquiry into the Human Mind on the Principle of Common Sense. Montana, Kessinger Publishing, LLC.

Roberts, H., Smith, S.J. and Lloyd, M. (1992). 'Safety as a Social Value: A Community Approach'. In eds Scott, S., Williams, G., Platt, S. and Thomas, H. (1992) Private Risks and Public Dangers. London, Avebury.

Smith, Sir, J.C. and Hogan (1999). Criminal Law: Cases and Materials. 7th Edition. London, Butterworths.

Steinberg, E. (1993). An Enquiry Concerning Human Understanding. Hume 1772. Indiana, Hackett Publishing.

Stoop, J and Dekker, S. (2009). Accident Modelling from Symptom to System. In Eds de Waar, D. et al. (2010). Human Factors : A system view of human, technology and organisation. Maastricht, Shaker Publishing.

Stufflebeam, D.L. and Shinkfield, A.J. (2007). Evaluation Theory, Models & Applications. San Francisco, Jossey-Bass.

Suchman, E, A. (1967). Evaluative Research: Principles and Practice in Public Service and Social Action Programs. New York, Russell Sage Foundation.

Tuckett, D. and Kaufert, J.M. (Eds) (1978). Basic Readings in Medical Sociology. London, Tavistock Publications Ltd.

Van der Schaaf, T.W. and Kanse, L. (2000). Errors and Error Recovery. In Eds Elzer, P.F., Kluwe, R.H. and Boussoffara, B. Human Error and System Design and Management. Lecture notes in control and information sciences. 253. London, Springer-Verlag.

Doyle, A.C. (1894). Memoirs of Sherlock Holmes. New York, Harper & Brothers. p.130.

Wiegmann, D.A. and Shappell, S.A. (2003). A Human Error Approach to Aviation Accident Analysis. Aldershot, Ashgate Publishing Ltd.

Williams, T. (2010/2011). These references relate to the IIAI Executive Committee Fellowship Lectures.

Woods, D.D., Dekker, S., Cook, R., Johannesen, L. and Sarter, N. (2008). Behind Human Error. 2nd Ed. Farnham, Ashgate Publishing.

Wright, L.B. and van der Schaaf, T.W. (2005) 'Near Miss Versus Accident Causation in the UK Railway'. In Eds. Wilson, J.R., Norris, B. and Mills, A. Rail Human Factors: Supporting The Integrated Railway. Aldershot, Ashgate Publishing Ltd.

Zohar, D. (1997). Rewiring the Corporate Brain. Using new science to rethink how we structure and lead organisations. San Francisco, Brett-Koehler Publications Inc.

PUBLICATIONS & PAPERS

Abdelhamid, T.S., and Everett, J.G. (2005). *"Identifying Root Causes of Construction Accidents"*. Journal of Construction Engineering and Management. 60. Jan/Feb.

Adams, E. (1976). *"Accident Causation and the Management System"*. Professional Safety. 10. ASSE.

Ajzen, I. (1991) *"The Theory of Planned Behaviour"*. Organizational Behaviour and Human Decision Processes. 50, 179-211.

Bogner, M.S. (2002). *"Stretching the search for the 'why' of error: the systems approach"*. Journal of Clinical Engineering. 110-115. Spring 2002.

Bogner (2004). Misadventures in Health Care: Inside Stories. Mahwah, Lawrence Erlbaum Associates Inc.

Broadbent, A. (2008). *"The Difference between Cause and Condition"*. Proceedings of the Aristotelian Society. Vol. 108. 355-364.

Bruggink, G.M. (1975). *"The Last Line of Defence"*. Legal Eagle News. Vol. 17. 7.

BSI (2004). BS 8800: "Occupational health and safety management systems-Guide". BSI.

BSI (2007). "BS OHSAS 18001: 2007. Occupational health and safety management systems-Requirements Guide". BSI.

BSI (2008). "Occupational health & safety management systems – Guidelines for the implementation of OHSAS 18001: 2007. 2nd Edition. BSI.

CAIB (2003). Columbia Accident Investigation Board (2003). Report Volume 1. [http://caib.nasa.gov/news/report/volume1/chapters.html].

Chapanis, A. (1991). *"To Communicate the human-factors message, you have to know what the message is and how to communicate it"*. Human Factors Society Bulletin. Nov. (34). 1-4.

Clarke, D.D., Ward, P., Bartle, C. and Truman, W. (2005). "An In-depth Study of Work-related Road Traffic Accidents". Road Safety Research Report No. 58. London, Department for Transport.

CM 6497. Corporate Manslaughter: The Government's Draft Bill for Reform. Norwich, TSO.

Cmnd. (5034). Safety and Health at Work: Report of the Committee 1970-72. Chairman, Lord Robens. London, HMSO.

Committee on Science and Technology (1986). "Investigation of the Challenger Accident: Report of the Committee on Science and Technology House of the Representatives". Washington, US Government Printing Office.

Cook, R.I., Woods, D.D. and Miller, C. (1998). *"A Tale of Two Stories; Contrasting Views of Patient Safety"*. Illinois, National Patient Safety Council at the AMA.

Fansler, T.E. (1959). *"The Dynamics of the Traffic Accident"*. The Traffic Review. Sept. 24-25.

Fischoff, B. (1975). *"Hindsight ≠ Foresight: The effect of outcome knowledge on judgement under uncertainty"*. Journal of Experimental Psychology (Human Perception and Performance. 1. Aug. 288-299.

Free, R. (1994). *The role of procedural violations in railway accidents.* Unpublished Doctoral Dissertation.

Froggatt, P. and Smiley, J.A. (1964) "The Concept of Accident Proneness: A Review". British Journal of Industrial Medicine. 21, 1. 1-12.

Fuller, R. (1990). *"Learning to Make Errors: Evidence from a Driving Simulation"*. Ergonomics. (33), 1241-1250.

Gordon, J.E. (1949). *"The Epidemiology of Accidents"*. American Journal of Public Health. 39. 504-515.

Gyekye, S.A. (2006) *"Causal Attributions for Industrial Accidents: A Culture-Comparative Analysis"*. In Ed. Allwood, J. Journal of Intercultural Communication. 11: 2006. www.immi.se/intercultural/.

Habberley, J. S., Shaddick, C.A. and Taylor, D. H., (1986). 'A Behavioural Study of the Collision Avoidance Task in Bridge Watchkeeping'. Southampton, College of Marine Studies.

Hollnagel, E. (2008). " The Changing Nature of Risks". Accessed 12/3/11. http://hal.archivesouvertes.fr/docs/00/50/88/58/PDF/ Changingnatureofrisks.pdf

HSW (2011). Health and Safety at Work. UK, Reed Elsevier.

Hudson, P.T.W., Reason, J., Wagenaar, W.A., Bentley, P.D., Primrose, M. and Visser, J.P. (1994). Tripod-Delta: Proactive Approach to Enhanced Safety. Journal of Petroleum Technology. 46, 58-62.

ISO 9001:2008. "Quality management systems-Requirements". BSI

Krieger, N. (1994) *"Epidemiology and the web of causation; has anyone seen the spider?"*. Social Science and Medicine, Oct, 39(7), 887-903.

Lander, L., Eisen, E.A., Stentz, T.L., Spanjer, K.J., Wendland, B.E. and Perry, M.J. (2010). *"Near-miss reporting system as an occupational injury preventive intervention in manufacturing"*. Accessed 13/3/11. http://onlinelibrary.wiley.com/doi/10.1002/ ajim.20904/full.

Law Comm No.237. Law Commission (1996). Legislating the Criminal Code: Involuntary Manslaughter. Item 11 of the Sixth Programme of Law Reform: Criminal Law. London, The Stationery Office.

Lekberg, A.K. (1997). *"Different Approaches to Incident Investigation: How the Analyst Makes a Difference"*. Hazard Prevention. 33(4).

Lewycky, P. (1987). "Notes Toward an Understanding of Accident Causes". Hazard Prevention. Mar-Apr. 6-8.

Lipton, P. (1992) *"Causation Outside the Law"*. In Eds Gross, H. and Harrison, R. Jurisprudence Cambridge Essays. Oxford University Press. 127-148.

Loeb, P.D. and Clarke, W.A. (2009). *"The Cell Phone Effect on Pedestrian Fatalities"*. Elsevier. Transportation Research Part E. 45(1). 284-290.

McBroom, W.H. and Reed, F.W. (1992). "Toward a Reconceptualization of Attitude-Behavior Consistency". Social Psychology Quarterly. 55, 205-216.

McFarland, R.A. (1966). "Measurement of Human Factors in Accident Research". In Proceedings of 3rd AMA Congress on Environmental Health Problems. Washington, American Medical Association.

Parker, D., Reason, J.T., Manstead, A.S.R. and Stradling, S. (1995). "Driving Errors, Driving Violations and Accident Involvement". Ergonomics. 38, 1036-1048.

Patterson, T.T. (1950). *"The Theory of the Social Threshold"*. The Sociological Review. 42, 3. 53-68.

Pettigrew, T.F. (1979). *" The Ultimate Attribution Error"*. *Extending Allport's Cognitive Analysis of Prejudice*. Personality and Social Psychology Bulletin. 55. 461-476.

Porterfield, A.L. (1960). "Traffic fatalities, suicide and homicide". American Sociological Review. 25, 897-901.

Rasmussen, J. (1990). *"The Role of Error in Organizing Behavior"*. Ergonomics. Vol. 33(10). 1185-99.

Reason, J. (2000). *"Human error: models and management"*. BMJ, March 2000. 768-70. (open learn pages 119-121).

Reason, J., Hollnagel, E. and Paries J. (2006). *"Revisiting the Swiss Cheese Model of Accidents"*. Project Safbuild – EEC Note No, 13/06. Access on-line.

Report of Court No. 8074. Mv Herald of Free Enterprise. London, HMSO.

Rogers Commission (1986). "Report of the Presidential Commission on the Space Shuttle Challenger Accident." [http://history.nasa.gov/ rogersrep/v1ch3.htm].

Schmidt, J., Schmorrow, D. and Figlock, R. (2000). *"Human Factors Analysis of Naval Aviation Maintenance Related Errors"*. Proceeding of the IEA 2000/HFES 2000 Congress.

Senate Report (1912). "Titanic Disaster: Report of the Committee on Commerce- United Sates Senate". [http://www.senate.gov/artand history/history/resources/pdf /TitanicReport.pdf]

Suchman, E.A. (1961). *"A Conceptual Analysis of the Accident Phenomenon"*. Social Problems. Aug. 241-253.

Suchman, E.A. (1970). *"Accidents and Social Deviance"*. Journal of health and Social Behavior. 11, 1. 4-15.

Swuste (2008). "You will only see it, if you understand it" or occupational risk prevention from a management perspective". Human Factors and Ergonomics in Manufacturing. 18(4). On-line, Wiley InterScience.

Visser, E., Pijl, Y.J., Stolk, R.P., Neeleman, J. and Rosmalen, J.G.M. (2007). "Accident proneness: does it exist? A review and meta-analysis". Accident Analysis and Prevention. 39, 556-564.

Weaver, D. (1971). "*Symptoms of Operational Error*". ASSE. Oct. Professional Safety.

Woods, D.D. and Cook, R.I. (2002). "*Nine steps to move forward from error*". Cognition, Technology and Work 2002. 4: 137-144.

Wright, L.B. and van der Schaaf, T.W. (2004) "*Accident versus near-miss causation: A critical review of the literature, an empirical test in the UK railway domain and their implications for other sectors*".

UK, EU AND USA CASES

Commission of the European Communities v United Kingdom of Great Britain and Northern Ireland. Case C-127/05.

Donoghue v Stevenson (1932) AC 562 HL.

Empress Car Company (Abertillery) Ltd v National Rivers Authority [1998] 1 ALL ER 481.

(ICI): Imperial Chemical Industries Ltd v Shatwell [1964] UKHL 2.

Ginty v Belmont Building Supplies Ltd [1959] 1 ALL ER 414.

Lynn Gas & Electric Co v Meriden Fire Insurance Co. 33 N.E. 690 (Mass 1893).

Nettleship v Weston [1971] 3 ALL ER 581.

Pawsey v Scottish Union & National Insurance [1907].

R v Adomako [1995] 1 AC 171.

R v Chargot Ltd (t/a Contract Services) and others [2008] UKHL 73.

R v Cunningham [1957] 2 ALL ER 412.

R v F. Howe and Son (Engineers) Ltd [1998]. EWCA Crim 3154.

R v HTM [2007] 2 ALL ER 665

R v Norwest Holst Construction Ltd and Costain Ltd. Ruling No Case.

R v Williams (Jason John) [2010]. EWCA Crim 2552.

R v P&O European Ferries (Dover) Ltd (1990) 93 Cr App Rep 72.

Re *"The Herald of Free Enterprise"* Q.B.D. The Independent 18/12/87, (Transcript: Blackwell). As per judgement 1. Hirst J.

Smith v Baveystock and Company Ltd [1945] 1 ALL E.R. 531.

EU DIRECTIVES

Council Directive 89/391/EEC of 12 June 1989 on the introduction of measures to encourage improvements in the safety and health of workers at work.

UK ACTS

CMCH Act 2007. Corporate Manslaughter and Corporate Homicide Act 2007. c.19.

Criminal Procedure and Investigations Act 1996. c.25.

Criminal Procedure and Investigations Act 1996 (Code of Practice) 2005 Order. No. 985.

Health and Safety at Work etc Act 1974. c37.

Road Traffic Act 1988. c.52.

USA ACTS

Occupational, Safety and Health Act of 1970.

UK REGULATIONS

The Management of Health and Safety at Work Regulations 1999. SI 1999 No. 3242.

WEB SITES

Cameron (2009). Reducing the Impact and Burden of Health and Safety. [http://www.conservatives.com/News/Speeches/2009/12/David_Cameron_Reducing_the_burden_and_impact_of_health_and_safety.aspx].

Honore, A. (2010). Causation in Law. Stanford Encyclopaedia of Philosophy. Accessed 5/3/11. [http://plato.stanford.edu/entries/ causation-law/#CauRelConCauFac].

HSE W1. [http://www.hse.gov.uk/enforce/enforcementguide/pretrial/after-key.htm#]. Downloaded 15/2/11.

Independent (Re cocaine at NASA base). [http://www.independent.co.uk/news/world/americas/nasa-investigates-cocaine-found-at-facility-2242651.html#]

Manuele, F.A. (2011) Reviewing Heinrich-Dislodging Two Myths From the Practice of Safety. Professional Development Peer-Reviewed. http://www.asse.org/professionalsafety/pastissues/056/10/052_061_F2Manuele_1011Z.pdf (accessed 12/10/11).

Parliament (2001). Managing Human Error. Postnote 156. London, Parliament. http://www.parliament.uk/documents/post/pn156.pdf

Reason, J. (2000). http://www.patientsikkerhed.dk/fileadmin/user _upload/ documents/Publikationer/Udenlandske/HumanError ModelsAnd Management.pdf

Sherwood-Jones, B.M. (2009). "Human/Error Accidents: Unpacking the blunt end-changing our view of organisational accident." Taylor & Francis. Accessed via Google docs 6/3/11.

Swuste, P. (2007). *"Qualitative Methods for Occupational Risk Prevention Strategies, or Control Banding-Safety"*. Safety Science Monitor. Vol. 11. 2007. [http://ssmon.chb.kth.se/vol11/Issue3/ 8%20Swuste.pdf]. Accessed 29/3/11.

van Gorp, A. (2005). "Ethical Issues in Engineering Design: Safety and Sustainability". In Eds Kroes, P. and Meijers, A. Simon Stevin Series in the Philosophy of Technology. Vol. II. Delft University. [http://www. ethicsandtechnolog y.eu/images/uploads/VanGorp_ EthicalIssues_ EngineeringDesing_SafetySustainability.pdf]

SUBJECT INDEX

A

Accident/s

Acts;

unsafe; *4, 5, 11, 12, 14, 24, 26, 29, 32, 34, 38, 39, 48, 66, 70, 71, 72, 75, 76, 87, 96, 100, 102, 105, 106, 114, 132, 133, 134, 135, 141, 142, 147, 148, 155, 161, 181, 187, 191, 194.*

deliberate; *23, 38, 45, 48, 65, 72, 74, 76, 79, 81, 89, 102, 121, 122, 123, 124, 126, 127, 164, 165, 167, 182, 186, 190, 195.*

single; *142.*

Agent (also see causation); *4, 5, 83, 84, 92, 104, 106, 136, 158.*

Aggregation; *170, 171, 172, 182.*

Alcohol (see drugs and)

American Society of Safety Engineers; *124.*

Antecedent; *22, 26, 34, 35, 54, 74, 79, 80, 89, 104, 119, 120, 124, 127, 138, 139, 164, 165, 167, 182, 186, 190, 192, 193, 194, 196.*

Appeals to emotion; *66, 172, 172, 180, 195, 196.*

Artichoke model; *106.*

ASSE (see American Society of Safety Engineers)

Attitude; *28, 88, 174.*

Attribution (see causal attribution)

Audit; *5, 41, 55, 102, 131, 140, 141, 143, 146, 149, 162, 169, 184, 185, 186, 196.*

Auditor; *143.*

B

Barriers; *viii, 23, 64, 79, 99, 121, 127, 132, 137, 154, 155, 156, 157, 158, 159, 160, 161, 164, 177, 178, 182, 186, 190, 192.*

Behaviour; *1, 2, 6, 7, 9, 11, 12, 13, 14, 21, 28, 32, 34, 40, 44, 51, 57, 65, 66, 67, 70, 71, 73, 74, 75, 76, 78, 79, 81, 84, 85, 86, 88, 89, 90, 92, 96, 101, 103, 105, 106, 108, 114, 122, 124, 142, 151, 152, 153, 154, 161, 174, 176, 178, 179, 180, 181, 180, 194, 195, 196, 197, 198, 201.*

Bias (see hindsight and confirmation)

Big bang; *136, 184.*

Blame; *viii, 2, 11, 44, 57, 64, 66, 102, 104, 135, 145, 149, 152, 153, 154, 157, 163, 168, 170, 172, 173, 174, 175, 179, 180, 181, 182, 201.*
    transference of; *157, 182.*

Blunt-end; *52, 80, 143, 151, 157, 158, 170.*

BP; *160.*

British Psychological Society; *90.*

BS8800; *139, 143.*

C

Calculator; *9, 140, 190.*

Cameron, prime minister, UK; *111.*

Causal Attribution;
    dispositional; *57, 58.*
    situational; *57, 67, 153, 174, 179.*

Causal chain (also see antecedent); *2, 13, 22, 70, 74, 76, 84, 92, 99, 102, 119, 130, 136, 137, 152, 158, 159, 190, 191, 198.*

Causation;
    agent (also see human agency)
    philosophy of; *vii, viii, xi, 2, 7, 10, 20, 26, 32, 40, 58, 87, 91, 99, 132, 134, 136, 142, 144, 148, 149, 160, 161, 163, 169, 171, 172, 182, 183, 184, 193, 197.*
    web of ; *3, 84, 85.*

Causal network; *3, 92.*

Cause;
    active and efficient; *74.*
        Lynn Gas v Meriden and; *74.*
    and effect; *24, 37, 44, 133.*
    indirect; *75.*
    intervening; *74, 163, 164.*
    over-lapping; *23, 102, 192, 167* (also see transitive).
    proximate; *4, 5, 13, 14, 21, 23, 30, 48, 52, 54, 70, 71, 72, 73, 74, 75, 81, 93, 96, 105, 122, 123, 125, 142, 148, 175, 183, 185, 186, 188, 193, 194, 195.*

relevant, limit of (also see tracing below); *104, 120.*

root; *viii, xi, 4, 18, 26, 30, 31, 37, 38, 39, 40, 53, 54, 55, 79, 87, 89, 96, 111, 119, 122, 127, 133, 136, 137, 138, 139, 143, 147, 148, 149, 159, 160, 162, 182, 184, 185, 186, 187, 190, 192, 197* (also see proximate cause).

sub; *22, 26, 28, 34, 38, 39, 75, 189.*

sufficient; *136.*

systemic; *139.*

tracing (also see relationships); *8, 53, 72, 74, 79, 81, 97, 106, 120, 121, 126, 127, 136, 159, 164, 165, 181, 190, 193, 195.*

barrier and goal; *79, 121, 127, 160, 164, 182, 190, 192.*

transitive; *vii, 23, 25, 26, 34, 35, 79, 97, 102, 104, 127, 165, 182, 183, 185, 190, 192, 193, 195, 196.*

underlying; *4, 13, 23, 26, 38, 39, 40, 48, 51, 52, 53, 75, 111, 176, 195, 196.*

Causes and conditions;

distinguishing between; *vii, 8, 37, 54, 164.*

Chain saw; *20.*

Challenger (Space shuttle); *51, 52, 53, 130, 138, 186.*

Chargot, R v; *31, 42, 48, 64, 110.*

Classical theorists (see school)

Classification schemes; *90.*

Cocaine (see drugs and alcohol)

Columbia (Space shuttle); *53.*

Common cause hypothesis

Heinrich; *4, 12, 13, 14, 15, 16.*
erroneous rejection of; *18, 20, 23, 25, 54, 96, 133.*

Common man; *104, 180.*

Complacency; *153.*

Condition/s;

complex set of; *119, 165.*

latent; *9, 51, 52, 53, 64, 66, 81, 87, 89, 90, 91, 126, 132, 134, 136,*
137, 140, 141, 143, 146, 147, 148, 149, 150, 151, 162, 163,
164, 165, 166, 169, 170, 177, 181, 182, 183, 184, 185, 186,
187, 188, 193, 195, 200.

mere; *3, 41, 44, 45, 48, 50, 51, 52, 53, 63, 64, 66, 80, 140, 141,*
147, 150, 163, 169, 190.

'necessary'; *27, 44, 119, 120, 130, 133, 135, 154, 162.*

unsafe; *11, 24, 26, 34, 35, 39, 71, 76, 99, 142, 191, 194.*

Confirmation bias; *viii, 17, 59, 66, 67, 126, 148, 183, 186, 188, 197.*

Construction; *20, 29, 30, 49, 50, 62, 101, 155, 171, 172, 236.*

Court of Appeal; *40, 65, 112.*

Crown, and prosecution service; *31, 65, 87, 113, 115.*

D

Deepwater Horizon; *149, 160, 186.*

Defences, in depth; *157.*

Deliberate act (see acts)

Department for Transport; *174.*

Digby effect; *41, 66, 67.*

Directors; *170, 171, 197, 201, 236.*

Discovery (Space shuttle); *101.*

Disease; *2, 83, 84, 171, 195.*

Domino sequences;
Bird; *6, 18, 97, 98, 99, 100, 101, 102, 103, 108, 149, 177,*
191, 192.
Difford; *73, 81.*
Grose; *97.*
Heinrich; *5, 11, 13, 69, 70, 71, 72, 73, 77, 78, 191, 194.*
Suchman; *78.*
Weaver; *96.*

Downstream (see factors)

Driving; *40, 47, 79, 156.*
and error and violation; *173, 174.*

Drugs and alcohol; *100, 101.*

man (see man, failure)

management (see management and management failure)

organisational; *xi, 4, 18, 22, 74, 103, 106, 122, 127, 132, 138, 149.*

random/intermittent; *22, 24, 25, 80, 157, 190.*

system (see system)

Fall;

from height; *142, 149.*

slip, trip and; *14, 21, 61, 63.*

Florida Space Centre; *101.*

Free will; *1, 67, 101, 103, 104, 105, 110, 136, 179.*

Functioning;

normal/abnormal; *45, 48, 49, 141, 151.*

usual/unusual; *46, 164.*

G

Ginty v Belmont; *152.*

God, act of; *11, 12, 27, 71, 73, 81, 161, 178.*

Group think; *58, 197.*

H

Hazards;

mechanical; *74.*

Health and Safety at Work etc Act 1974 *(see Parliament, UK)*

Health and Safety Executive (UK); *6, 7, 30, 31, 34, 40, 42, 43, 48, 85, 86, 87, 88, 89, 90, 91, 92, 101, 107, 109, 110, 111, 112, 113, 114, 115, 132, 134, 161, 172, 175, 179, 188, 197, 201.*

Director General of; *30, 31.*

Heinrich;

accident causation theory, basic premise of; *71.*

injury severity ratios; *15.*

study, general; *69.*

Herald of Free Enterprise; *91, 130, 131, 150, 151, 153, 154, 170.*

Heroes; *171, 172.*

Hindsight bias; *viii, 65, 67, 197.*

Holmes, Sherlock (see digby effect)

Host; *4, 5, 83, 84, 92.*

Howe, R v; *20.*

HSE (see Health and Safety Executive UK)

HSG48; *86, 87, 88, 89, 90, 157.*

HSG65; *87, 89, 107, 108, 109, 111, 112.*

HSG245; *38, 138.*

HTM, R v; *110, 112.*

Human (also see behaviour)
> agency (see agent)
> element; *106, 109, 157, 179.*
> error (also see driving); *viii, 3, 6, 7, 16, 19, 22, 27, 30, 38, 40, 60, 64, 65, 66, 72, 78, 79, 86, 89, 90, 96, 97, 99, 100, 103, 104, 105, 106, 112, 114, 130, 131, 132, 133, 134, 135, 136, 137, 140, 141, 142, 145, 146, 156, 160, 161, 162, 170, 171, 173, 174, 175, 179, 180, 185, 186, 195, 236.*

> error as a consequence; *7, 105, 114, 130.*
> factors; *86, 179, 198.*

Hypothesis; *4, 13, 14, 15, 16, 18, 19, 20, 23, 25, 27, 54, 96, 132, 133, 178.*

I

Iceberg; *141, 151.*
> theories; *19.*

IIAI (see Institute of Industrial Accident Investigators)

Indistinguishable, theories; *23.*

Injury;
> disabling; *29.*
> fatal; *13, 17, 29, 30, 32, 50, 70, 110, 149, 158, 236.*
> minor; *15, 17, 19, 20, 27.*
> major; *12, 13, 15, 105.*
> severe; *17, 19, 20, 24, 25.*

227

Man;

> common (see common man)
> failure; *15, 150.*
> in the street; *114, 134.*
> reasonable; *v, 4.*
> *also see sharp-end/blunt-end.*

Maintenance; *30, 31, 99, 146.*

Management;

> failure test; *152.*
> of Health & Safety at Work Regulations; *112.*

Management failures; *vii, xi, 5, 6, 8, 9, 17, 26, 29, 30, 31, 32, 35, 38, 39, 41, 42, 52, 88, 89, 95, 96, 99, 100, 107, 114, 124, 127, 131, 133, 134, 152, 162, 178, 194.*

Managers; *37, 42, 62, 77, 89, 93, 103, 136, 139, 143, 145, 153, 154, 170, 171, 174, 187, 197.*

Manchester University; *147.*

Manslaughter; *152.*

Maritime (also see shipping and offshore)

Mere Condition (see condition)

Metaphor (see resident pathogen)

Mishap; *27, 35, 160, 161, 181.*

Multiple Causation;

> theory, essential premise of; *22, 24, 28.*
> crime and; *1.*
> epidemiology and; *2.*

N

NASA; *52, 53, 101, 149.*

National Safety Council; *17, 19.*

Natural phenomena/phenomenon; *1, 81, 104, 195.*

NEBOSH; *111.*

Negative evidence; *80.*

Negligence; *40, 111, 152, 153.*

service provision; *173.*

Nelson, R v; *110.*

Nettleship v Weston; *47.*

Neucom; *vii.*

Neucom Ltd; *34, 189, 195, 236.*

New Millennium Theory, Difford's; *viii, 10, 58, 189, 194.*

Norwest, R v; *65, 198.*

O

Occupational, Safety and Health Act 1970; *17, 59.*

Offshore; *27, 31, 158, 236.*

Omission; *11, 14, 34, 54, 97, 105, 142, 154.*

Operational;

definition; *74, 78, 79, 80, 121, 160.*
negligence; *152.*

Operational error; *27, 96.*

Organisational accident (see accident)

Organisational hierarchy; *157, 170.*

Organizational model of human error; *103.*

OSHA; *17.*

P

P&O, R v; *152.*

Parliament (UK)

Health and Safety at Work etc Act 1974; *2, 59.*
Office of Science and Technology; *90, 91, 150, 188.*

Pawsey v Scottish Union; *74.*

Person model (Reason's so-called); *163.*

Philosophy (see under causation)

Plea;

bargaining; *109.*

Robens, Lord; *30, 75, 85, 92.*

Root cause; *viii, xi, 4, 18, 26, 30, 31, 37, 38, 39, 40, 53, 54, 55, 79, 87, 89, 96, 111, 119, 122, 125, 127, 133, 136, 137, 138, 139, 143, 147, 148, 149, 159, 160, 162, 182, 184, 185, 186, 187, 190, 192, 197.*

Roulette, Russian; *171.*

S

Safety;

achievement of; *105.*
indicators; *5, 102, 123, 144, 145, 146, 147, 149, 160, 163, 184, 187.*

non-achievement of; *105.*
practitioners; *ix, 3, 18, 40, 42, 55, 84, 89, 110, 111, 132, 201.*
proofing; *85, 188.*

School;

classical theorists; *1.*
management failure; *vii, 8, 17, 32.*
organisational accident; *xi, 5, 9, 52.* (also see management failure)
positivist; *1.*

Self-interest; *48, 115, 195, 196.*

Self-supervision; *32, 33.*

Sequence (exceptionless causal); *xi, 5, 7, 8, 9, 10, 24, 34, 54, 72, 73, 74, 80, 81, 82, 101, 102, 114, 115, 124, 125, 127, 145, 163, 165, 180, 182, 183, 184, 185, 186, 188, 190, 192, 194.*

Sharp-end; *7, 52, 53, 57, 59, 67, 80, 122, 123, 127, 156, 157, 158, 170, 172.*

Shell; *70, 145, 158, 159, 160, 164.*

Sherlock, Holmes (see Holmes)

Shipping (also see maritime and offshore)

Smith v Baveystock; *152.*

Space shuttle (see Challenger, Columbia and Discovery)

Stephenson (see Donoghue)

Stop rule; *78, 79, 80, 136, 139.*

general failure types; *145, 146, 147, 148, 149, 187.*

Unconditional (causal sequence): *see sequence.*

Unions; *29, 33, 188.*

Unsafe Acts (see acts)

Upstream (see factors)

V

Violation; *viii, 7, 30, 31, 64, 86, 87, 88, 89, 99, 100, 105, 112, 114, 133, 134, 135, 136, 141, 142, 143, 145, 156, 162, 170, 173, 174, 178, 186.*

W

Web of causation (see causation)

Williams, R v; *40, 46, 47.*

Window; *13, 49, 57.*

Working environment (see environment)

Workplace; *5, 7, 29, 42, 49, 63, 72, 76, 100, 101, 103, 110, 127, 137, 144, 148, 149, 169, 175, 179, 184, 185, 187, 188, 201.*

Y

Young, Lord; *111.*

About the Author

As Director of Research & Development at the Institute of Industrial Accident Investigators, Paul has coordinated both of the Institute's Ten Year Studies and published numerous internal papers. This book, the first in a series of eagerly anticipated titles, is an output of that.

Paul is also a Director with UK based Neucom Ltd where he is the Senior HSQE Consultant and Principal Investigator. As a service Neucom provides, he assists criminal defence teams and organisations in the after-math of actual and potential high yield accidents. He completed his first fatal investigation more than 25 years ago and, in 2009, was instrumental in a successful conclusion to one of the decade's longest running criminal enquiries. Touching on that case and similar ones, Paul graphically compels the reader to confront the stark reality of industrial death, and its cause.

As an expert in causation and systems interrogation, his practical experience comes via International exposure to passenger and defence aviation, marine/off-shore environments, road & rail transport and military special forces. Comfortable in both the boardroom and the field, he understands risk across the entire corporate spectrum and has managed numerous construction and engineering projects. Sought after as a speaker, he lectures across a range of allied subjects from error analysis to investigative interviewing. Renowned as one of industry's no-nonsense, straight talkers, his writing style is unique, to the point and superbly informative.